DISCOVERING RECOVERY
From Mental Health Distress

The experiences of a mental health
support group

Dedication

This book is dedicated to the memory of Sheila B,
a lively member of the group for many years.

Her endless support for the group and its members
will never be forgotten.

DISCOVERING RECOVERY

by

The Rushcliffe Mental Health Support Group

Copyright (©) 2009

ISBN: 978-0-9559590-0-4

Published by the Rushcliffe Mental Health Support Group
in conjunction with Writersworld Ltd

Printed and bound by printondemand-worldwide.com

Copy edited by Sue Croft

www.writersworld.co.uk

WRITERSWORLD
2 Bear Close
Woodstock
Oxfordshire
OX20 1JX
United Kingdom

Rushcliffe Mental Health Support Group

We are a peer support group, based primarily in Rushcliffe, Nottinghamshire, for anyone affected by mental health problems.

Authors and contributors

Alex (pseudonym)

Ann (pseudonym)

Anon 1

Anon 2

Becky Shaw

Chris Heap

Eddie Brompton

Elizabeth (pseudonym)

Hugh Thomas

Editors
Becky Shaw and Hugh Thomas

The Lost Artists Club

The Lost Artists Club members are very pleased to contribute to 'Discovering Recovery'.

Photography by Clive Millwater, Secretary,
The Lost Artists Club

Dean Kemp

Sarah Pearce

Johanna Sharland

John Sharland

Corinne Smith

Richard Toon

Other Artists and Illustrators

Ann

Chris Heap

Anon

Cover artwork is by Richard Toon
Title of artwork is *Blue*, created using Mixed Media

Johanna Sharland, *Brain Storm*, Pencil

Disclaimer

This book is based on personal experience and personal views of the system.

Any information contained in it does not set out to replace medical and therapeutic treatment.

If you feel that you, or someone close to you, is suffering from depression or any other form of mental distress—ask for help. The sooner you receive the help you need, the sooner you will start the process of recovery.

If you do not know where to begin to get help and don't want to involve your GP or family, then one of the national self-help organizations such as Mind can help you talk it through.

Contents

Johanna Sharland, *Marshy Meadow,* **Encaustic art**

Introduction

It all began when I started the support group in 1995. This was my attempt at finding friends who would be supportive and who had experience of going through similar tough times. I had lost all my friends and needed support from people who would accept me for who I was, with all my faults. I had already found this support from my peer inmates on the mental health acute ward where I had spent seven months. I also realised about this time that there must be other people out there who also needed support. An opportunity to use a small amount of funding for starting a group arose and the Rushcliffe Mental Health Support Group was formed.

Over the last twelve years the group has changed its membership, but not its purpose. People come and go and use the group when needed. We have a saying that everything should be relaxed and without pressure, so nothing is obligatory and attendance is when you can. However, we have found that people nearly always want to attend regularly. It gives them something to look forward to and be involved in, especially the social activities that the group arranges. It is also a group that is run by its members and this is the process that I have facilitated and supported. I hate bowling, but if that is what the members want, I arrange it—even if it does take a year or so longer than is usual to arrange! The other main function of the group is to provide a space to share ideas about what has helped to support each other when struggling at times of distress. This has been not only through group meetings but also through email contact and newsletters for members who cannot, for whatever reason, make the meetings. There have also been meetings outside the group where members have shared information about themselves and helped practically, by putting up book cases and setting up DVD players and so on, and also emotionally through just being there, in person or on the phone.

So why are we writing this book?

We are writing this book so that we can share our learning from several areas.

- Firstly, to share the effect that the experience of a small support group can have on individuals

- Secondly, to share our experiences of what helps and what doesn't help when experiencing mental health distress

- Thirdly, to tell you about group members' individual experiences of mental health services

Finally, the aim of the entire book is to highlight *the recovery process* from mental health distress. It offers hope and optimism for those currently in distress, and tips for those people supporting them.

The journey to recovery is an ongoing path of discovery. All the contributors to this book are at different stages of their journey.

Becky Shaw (founder)

Johanna Sharland, *Steps of Eon*, Encaustic Art

Johanna Sharland, *Dark Mountain*, Encaustic Art

Sheila and Eddie's story

Sheila

I first became involved in the Health Service when my eldest daughter was born in the City Hospital in July 1964. Four months later I was in Mapperley Hospital with post-natal depression. I had six electric treatments (ECT) which were repeated the following February. My father died during my first course of treatments. I did not know anything about this at the time.

I still went periodically into Mapperley Hospital. At this time there was no real aftercare.

In September 1977 I had a baby who lived for 36 hours. I had been told 2 weeks before that the baby would not live. They looked after me really well at the City Hospital.

In 1988 I had a recurrence of mental health problems. I was in Queen's Medical Centre for eight months, going home at the weekend if I was well enough.

My psychiatrist sorted out my medication and I still take the same medication now.

I have had two side effects from one of the tablets. My thyroid was affected so now I take Thyroxine tablets. Also I put on 2 stone in weight while in hospital.

In 1993 I was found to have psoriasis and it also came with arthritis. I ended up being in Queen's for three weeks in Intensive Care with psoriasis. Since then I have had occasional treatment for it.

Since 1990 I have been attending a group run by 'George Road' (Rushcliffe Mental health team). I also go to a Support Group. I also went on a six-week course called The Expert Patient programme, a course run by the NHS. Most people had different types of illnesses and disabilities.

Eddie

You do not think that you are a Carer when you are married. You just think that is what you do.

Sheila went into Mapperley Hospital in December 1976. She was in for about 2 weeks. We did not have a very good Christmas that year.

The following year, when Sheila was pregnant, in September the hospital thought she was too big for how many weeks pregnant she was. They told us that our baby would not live, but they did not know if it would be born dead or alive. On 29 September 1977 Sheila had to have an emergency Caesarean section. We had a daughter whom we called Rachael. She lived for just 36 hours and ten minutes. The following week I had to go and register her as a Birth and Death. My mother came with me as I do not know that I could have coped on my own.

The following year we went to Genetic Counselling. They told us that there was a one in four risk of having a deformed child. So we decided not to try again.

In 1985 Sheila was not well again. This time she went straight into Queen's Medical Centre. Mental Health had moved on since 1976 and the staff did not wear white coats, just ordinary clothes.

While Sheila was in hospital it took a long time for her to get better. But once her medication was sorted out she improved a lot.

While Sheila was in QMC they started a Relatives' Support Group, which I went to. I found it very helpful. The only problem was that when my wife came home, that was it.

Then in 1990 the Rushcliffe Mental Health Team started a support group in the community and I have been a member ever since.

In about 1992 Sheila started to get arthritis and psoriasis. This was not a very nice condition. In 1993 Sheila went into the Dermatology unit at QMC for about three weeks. It helped for a time but it never clears up.

Although we have had a lot of problems, I would not change anything. We have done a lot of nice things together and we have had many nice holidays. We have also had a lot of support over the years from many different people.

Journeys

Life Before

We all had different experiences of what life was like before illness struck. Some, like me, had illness blacken their life at the tender age of 13. Others came to their illness much later in life. Whatever the circumstances, life before would usually have been completely different. Once illness arrives it is sometimes hard to remember what life was like before.

Hugh

I grew up in a happy, middle-class family with a father who was a teacher, a loving mother and a sister five years younger than me. I idolised my father and my sole aim was to do well in his eyes.

I passed the eleven plus a year early and moved to the grammar school. My father was now a headmaster. In the exams at the end of the first year I was top of the class. All the teachers and everyone else thought I was bound for Oxford or Cambridge. In the second year at grammar school I had rheumatic fever which kept me off school for six months. However my father arranged home tutors in some subjects and when I finally got back to school I caught up with my other subjects. At the end of exams I still managed to end up second in the class!

Becky

Life before I experienced any difficulties was like being on a treadmill, going nowhere and following the herd. I was expected to attend school, get my exams and go to university, then find a nice boy my parents would approve of, get married and have two children, settling down into the routine of life and being a part of society.

Although, until I was fifteen, I had had no contact with mental health services, I already had my difficulties. At the age of five I started to hear voices that no one else could hear—a male voice I called 'him', a friend and companion and very much as real as anyone I have ever met. He was one of those friends that at times you love and at other times you hate, but he was my only source of real friendship.

I learned very early on that it was wrong to hear things others couldn't, but to me it was an ordinary part of my life and I did not want to lose him. I grew up with him, as friendships with other children my own age were hard to find. I was bullied by children, even those who called themselves my friends. I was abused at various periods throughout my life, both when I was very young and as a teenager (emotionally and physically). A combination of all these factors meant I became isolated, cutting myself off from the world and from my own emotions. I talked to no one about what had happened and what was still happening to me. Then I went to university and this was where my world fell apart, hurling me headlong into my emotions for the first time and into the mental health services that have trapped me for so long now.

Anon

I have always felt different. At school I had a lot of friends but something wasn't right. What kept me going and on track was that I thought things would get better when I could make my own choices. My suicidal thoughts happened when things were finally looking good, for some reason. I was working really hard at the time and by night I was crying, for no apparent reason. I thought things had hit the lowest point but little did I know that things would get a lot worse.

First I thought my phone calls were being listened into and then I thought hidden cameras were watching me. I gave up work suddenly and relocated. Things got worse still as I started to hear voices. They gradually increased their frequency. I wasn't telling the doctor this as I thought everybody was part of a conspiracy.

Ann

I am now aged 52 and, looking back on my life, I remember having some very sad and some happy times. One of the major crisis times for me was not passing my 11+ exam. I felt a failure and lost some of my good friends because they went to the High School and I went to the Secondary School. However, I knew a girl who lived near us who had attended the Secondary School, done well in her CSEs and transferred to the High School to do "A" Levels, so I hung on and hoped this might happen for me.

I remember feeling dreadful whilst waiting for my CSE results, so much so that I started asking myself what life was all about. I visited my grandfather during this time and wondered why he seemed so content with life, as he carried on day by day doing the same old things.

I didn't have any really close friends as a teenager. Other girls in my class had boyfriends; were prettier; had better parents than me; were good at sports; had lovely hair; more fashionable clothes; cleverer than me etc. etc. I wanted to be anybody else but me. I felt as though I had no self-worth. Having had psychotherapy and counselling, I now look back and know that those feelings and thoughts were unsubstantiated. Maybe if I had had a really close friend or sister, or had been able to talk easily with my parents, I may have been able to rationalise these thoughts.

Before I had my first breakdown I took everything people said to me to heart. I tried to please everyone and had not given much thought to myself. For example, I always made sure everything was clean and that everything was done in the correct way. Negative comments were taken on board far more than positive comments. I have since learnt that no one can live up to those standards, and that trying to do so may cause a nervous breakdown.

Chris

Although I had undetected episodes of psychosis when I was in my early twenties, and possibly during childhood, the full-blown event that resulted in hospitalisation, medication and the rest didn't come until my mid-thirties. Prior to this I had been living in Sweden for almost 10 years. During my time in Scandinavia I had a relationship with a Swedish girl, had a good social life, plenty of interests such as reading, art, walking, fishing, sports etc. I studied at university to Master's degree level, focusing on animal ecology. I also held a position as a field/admin worker at the university as well as working part-time as an English teacher.

The relationship with my girlfriend had been rocky for about 5 years prior to my hospitalisation and towards the end of the relationship my mother was diagnosed with motor neurone disease, with no hope of a cure. Her life expectancy was 15 months! During that time I was juggling study and work in Sweden with long visits to England to be close to my mother during her final time. Looking back, this was a very stressful and sad time. My mother died in early 2004 whilst I was in Sweden.

Following my mother's death I had a tough time living in Sweden, just keeping going. I would say I was no fun to be around as I was experiencing a mixture of grief, anger, sadness and withdrawal. My relationship took a serious nose dive at this point, as did I. I suppose in

12

many ways I just gave up. My life felt as if it was going out of control. Before I knew what had happened I found myself living in England in a shared house, working part-time doing painting and decorating, drinking quite a lot and dabbling in party drugs.

It is difficult to pinpoint exactly when my voyage into psychosis began, but it was sometime during the summer of 2005. I ended the relationship with my girlfriend in Sweden and went well and truly off the rails.

A mixed bag

So there is a mixed bag here; some people felt happy and normal before illness hit, some of us felt pressured to achieve a strenuous kind of lifestyle; others always felt different. But there is no doubt that the onset of mental health problems changed everybody's life dramatically. There seems to be a mixture of optimism and pessimism in people's stories.

Where to turn when things get rough

Knowing where to turn is of vital importance. The first logical step would be to contact your family GP. This can be a bit of a lottery since a general practice doctor's knowledge and experience of mental health problems can be limited. The situation is better than it used to be but still there is a lack of awareness among some practitioners. With luck the GP will refer you on to a psychiatrist and this is where you will get into the system where, hopefully, you will get the help and advice you need.

Ann

My first breakdown occurred seven months after the birth of our first son, John. John was born with a sight difficulty, and until he could talk to us we had no idea how much or little he could see. Our GP was very good, but in the end felt a psychiatrist was needed. He prescribed Dothiepin and I met him several times as an outpatient. I don't remember being given a diagnosis and didn't feel he was helping very much, so after a few appointments with him, I discharged myself.

Our GP and my health visitor were my life-savers on this first occasion and slowly I recovered. I accepted that, with a baby, my routine had to change and I settled into tackling one job a day, for example ironing, dusting, or cleaning, while making sure we were fed, had clean clothes and so on. But most importantly I had to make sure that I rested.

When I had the second baby, I even tried to have an afternoon sleep with him and my other little one. Most days, when the boys were young, we'd go out to the park, the shops, the library etc. I would try and make these outings as interesting as possible. We would stop and look at cobwebs, different coloured leaves or big diggers going about their work. With John, the older of our two boys, who had limited vision, I would have to bring the world to him e.g. picking up a leaf or a caterpillar and putting them in his hands, standing as close as possible to watch a big digger or see a car (he loved cars). I slowly stopped worrying about the house. A possible contributory factor to this first depressive episode was people in the street commenting to me "your baby looks tired". My health visitor solved this problem. She said, "tell them". I plucked up courage and did tell them. The first time was the most difficult and I was surprised when most people had a similar tale to share. It was a huge relief to be open and honest.

I accessed the services for a second time when we moved from London to Nottingham (5 years after the first episode). It was much worse and I felt very suicidal. We had moved into a new house and my husband had opened his new snack bar all in the same week. I was trying to help him with the snack bar, cope with the children and sort out the new house all at the same time—recipe for disaster. I wasn't sleeping very well or eating very well (I lost 2 stone in 2 months) and it all seemed too much. I convinced myself that the world would be a better place without me and took an overdose of paracetamol. I rang the Samaritans because I wanted them to arrange for my parents to collect the boys from school. The Samaritans were happy to do this but convinced me that I needed help, and in the end, I let them call an ambulance for me.

Anon, *Where To Turn? Charcoal*

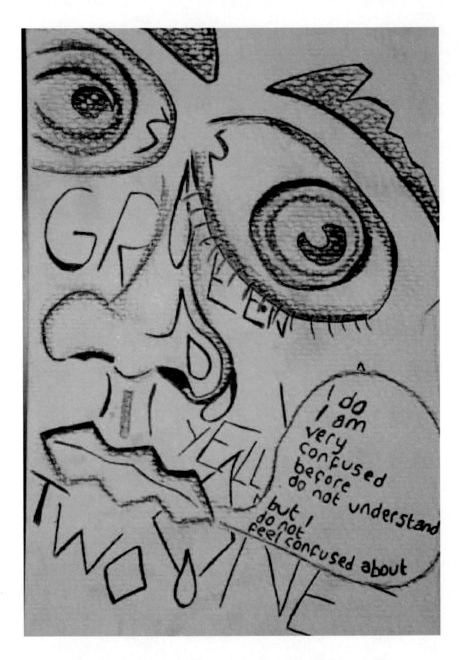

Sarah Pearce, *W O*, Green Eye Pencil (pencil)

Hugh

At the end of the third year of school, at the end of the summer holidays, I was doing some schoolwork at home ready for the fourth year when I suddenly had an awful headache and found I could not concentrate on what I was doing. I panicked. I got on my bike to get my mother; I didn't know what was going on! I attempted to start the new academic year at school but the symptoms persisted. Eventually I was taken to see my family GP. He didn't know what was wrong with me but eventually prescribed phenobarbitone. I was bewildered. He was an excellent GP and the family had had him as a doctor for the whole of my life, but he obviously didn't have any psychiatric training.

My school work suffered and I had many periods off school with illness. I scraped two A levels and went to work in a bank.

Life at the bank was like life at school—lots of time off with illness—the illness I didn't understand at all! Eventually I was really ill and my church minister thought I should see a psychiatrist. He recommended one he knew well and so we suggested this to the GP. An appointment was made and so I got to have my first visit with a psychiatrist. He was very good, very understanding and easy to talk to. I felt a huge sense of relief that I could get so much off my chest. I saw him many times and he was a great help.

Becky

Recurrent clinical depression, psychosis, self-harm, bulimia and anxiety are the main symptoms of the mental health distress I experience. Life varies from day to day and week to week. Some days I feel like I can conquer the world and other days I can barely bring myself to make a cup of tea or find the energy to get out of bed. I manage my life on how I am feeling and I am getting better at knowing when I should stop and take a break. Sometimes this might mean stopping altogether and going for respite, whereas at other times it might mean a few days or hours resting and taking time for me. If I did not manage my up and down life in this way I would become acutely unwell and end up back on a mental health acute ward or worse, dead.

The causes of this distress lie in the roots of my past, through emotional and physical abuse. I now, however, have a future and, although I have my difficulties, I give back what I can through voluntary work and by helping with my peer support group. This gives my life meaning and purpose, something a lot of us take for granted as I certainly did before I was acutely unwell, and this also gives me a reason to live, and a love of life again, especially when I am on an 'up' day.

At first I just knew I needed help. I wanted someone to talk things through with about the abuse and my childhood. I went to my GP but didn't know what to say so I waffled about other things and never really said what I needed to. Admitting something is wrong is the first step but I hadn't really done that. I knew something wasn't right. The drinking had got out of control and my self-harming was more extreme, but I didn't know where to turn. I wanted someone to talk things through with and that happened to be my GP's nurse who just took that extra time to enquire how I was. She was gentle and kind whenever she saw me and took things slowly. She didn't force me to see the GP but asked if I wanted her to talk to him first and also suggested which GP I should see.

GPs, as you might already know, are better at some things than others. Some GPs like the elderly, some the young, and some mental health and wellbeing. So the first step for me was having someone who cared and wanted to help and took the time to listen to what I wanted and needed. There was no pressure and no judgement on the nurse's part. She just wanted to help.

Seeing the psychiatrist for the first time was scary and unnerving. I paced the entrance hall. I didn't want to go in. My head was full of questions, buzzing with thoughts and concerns. What would he think of me? Would he lock me up? Should I even be here? I wanted to go, to get out of that place as soon as I entered. Those five minutes' waiting were the longest of my life.

I was called through and he seemed nice, but where was the couch I had expected? Instead there were three chairs and I was shown to one. Forty minutes went fast. I felt guarded as if I my every word was being examined—which it was, of course. I came out with a prescription for antidepressants, one I did not want but felt obliged to take as if some magic tablet might help take away the distress. Forty minutes had passed so quickly and resulted in what? **A box of pills**.

Anon

It was a year after I had given up work that I was referred to a psychiatrist. I had virtually given up hope and I wasn't entirely sure if I was ill or if everyone else was. When I saw the psychiatrist I thought she was an actor, due to my delusions, and that the whole setup was a humiliating joke. That said, she was very nice but she asked direct questions I hadn't been expecting, which were a bit close to the bone. Later that day she came round to my house with my GP and a social worker and they said I should go to hospital.

I wasn't sure whether or not I had the choice, but when I d been in for a day or two and said I wanted to go home, they said I wasn't allowed.

Chris

I first came into contact with a panel of doctors in Stonehouse police station in Stroud, Gloucestershire, during the summer of 2005. I had no idea what the time was and it was dark. I had not seen a solicitor, had no contact with the outside world and I had given a DNA sample.

I was afraid. Very afraid. I did not know who I could trust. I had a delusional belief at the time that some of the police officers were in fact aliens masquerading as human police, that they wanted to kill me, and that these 'alien police' were being closely watched and analysed by human police.

So my first access to mental health services consisted of me being led out of a cell and shown into a room where a panel of four health-workers (probably including social workers and psychiatrists) made an assessment of my mental state. They asked me numerous questions, of which I recall none, and eventually concluded that I was sane and able to undergo police questioning about alleged offences of criminal damage, resisting arrest and assaulting a police officer. I should add here that I believed this police officer was an alien and that he rugby-tackled me after chasing me, and tried to spray gas in my face.

At the time of my detention and mental health assessment I was very adept at masking or hiding my beliefs. I was extremely delusional and hallucinatory at this time. I was suffering a psychotic episode and was under a lot of mental and emotional pressure. It almost goes without saying that I do not think these mental-health workers made an accurate assessment of my mental state and so I would not regard this as the first occasion I received help. This didn't happen until one-and-a half years later, after a period in which I had worked full-time as a recycler driver, had driven back to Sweden to collect my belongings, lived in four different houses and had three, brief, failed relationship attempts—oh yes, and suffered my worst depression up to that point, which lasted for about six months. I withdrew into myself during this time into a very dark and lonely place, with a sense of hopelessness, flatness, complete lack of interest in life, and suicidal thoughts.

However, during this time I still remained undiagnosed and had no contact with mental health services. I was expected by the Department of Works and Pensions to actively seek work and eventually took a job which lasted three months.

Life seemed to pick up briefly, but what I was not aware of at the time was that I was entering into a manic phase that would last almost four months. Suddenly I had money and was in a working situation where I was socializing again, although a lot of the time I was deluded and withdrawn. This is socially unacceptable and can make you feel paranoid and excluded, believing others think you are weird. I began drinking too much, probably to mask or alter my mind-set, and I had some scary bouts of paranoia.

Before long I was signed off sick with stress and a chest infection. I was prescribed Zopiclone by my GP to help me sleep and she was even close to giving me Valium to calm me down. However, as she warned me of the possible addictive nature of this drug, I chose not to take it. During this period I had a lot of time on my hands and began going out, taking cocaine and ecstasy on occasions as well as drinking a lot. Eventually I was arrested for smashing up a dilapidated greenhouse in which I believed there were evil spirits.

The police took me to an observational cell where I was left for about an hour. Some plain-clothed person sat outside and I had no idea of his role. There were also numerous plain-clothed people moving around in the corridors and I had no idea what was taking place. In the cell I became convinced that some girl had been gang-raped by five or six men at some time in the past and in my deluded state I began lashing out at what I believed were negative energies lingering in the cell. Four police officers, two with riot shields, forced me down onto a mattress on the floor.

From then on I recall nothing. I had a 24-hour blackout. I must have been forcibly injected with some kind of tranquiliser. I woke up mid-afternoon in a single bed in a room, with a pair of donated jeans at the bottom of my bed. I got up and dressed, walked out of the room and down a corridor, to find myself on a psychiatric ward in Bath. I was not aware of it at the time but I had been detained under Section 2 of the Mental Health Act (I do not recall any kind of mental health assessment prior to sectioning).

After four days on this ward I got to see a consultant psychiatrist and we had a twenty minute discussion, at the end of which I was discharged without a diagnosis or prescription for any kind of meds. I suppose I had stabilised sufficiently or wasn't deemed ill enough to stay on the ward, and in any case I was happy to be discharged although at that time I was still quite manic and had no insight into my condition.

The first signs

Because the first indications of mental health difficulties are a bewildering and frightening experience, the first obvious port of call is the family general practitioner. However, as you can tell from the above accounts, unfortunately many GPs do not have a comprehensive knowledge or experience of mental health problems. If a GP does his or her job properly he or she will try to deal with the immediate symptoms, and if that fails will refer a patient immediately to a psychiatrist. Family and friends are an immediate form of support, but unless they have a good knowledge of mental health difficulties and of the mental health system, they are seldom of any real assistance.

Richard Toon, *Sleep & Dreams*, Mixed Media

Psychosis

What is psychosis?

Psychotic experiences

Psychosis usually refers to experiences where the person 'loses touch with reality'.

The types of experience can include:
- Hearing voices when no one is there
- Seeing or sensing things others do not
- Holding strong beliefs that others in the community do not share (often called 'delusions') and sometimes these delusions include the belief that others are out to harm you (called 'paranoid delusions')
- Experiencing extreme moods, e.g. depression, elation or both at the same time
- Changes in perception, e.g. seeing colours much more brightly than usual
- Feeling much better or worse about one's self than normal
-

Some people may also:
- Find it hard to concentrate on things
- Appear distracted or 'talk back' to the voices
- Talk in a way which is hard to follow, for example quickly moving from topic to topic
- Feel withdrawn, listless, apathetic or unmotivated

Psychotic experiences

Becky

I like to think of my psychosis as real for me, as after all it is my reality, although it is not in the shared reality of other people around me.

Chris

This is a complex world to unravel and explain. To write about it feels like baring my soul. It feels very personal and it is something that I have found difficult to open up about. I have told my girlfriend about it in some detail, but it was easier to be open with her about it as she has had her own experiences of psychosis. My consultant psychiatrist also has fragments of information about it, having seen me during a manic episode, and also talked with me about it during remission, but he far from knows the whole story. I have also shared some details of my psychotic experiences with my counsellor, who was the first person without any mental health issues that I have told. It was quite liberating to share with her.

My own experience of psychosis is rather mixed up. I had delusions of reference; severe and prolonged paranoia; delusions of grandeur or that I was chosen for some higher spiritual purpose like protector of Christ at the Second Coming; feelings of persecution; conspiratorial thoughts and sensations of being watched. I have believed I was working undercover for the police tracking down sex offenders and fighting evil spirits and demons. For some time I mentally and emotionally inhabited a world of good vs evil, a world populated by demons, vampires, aliens and such, disguised as humans. At times this world was terrifying and I envisaged that some hideous, torturous death lay in store for me. At other times I felt protected and powerful enough to face and challenge the evil.

While on the brink of and during psychosis I met numerous people who re-affirmed my delusionary thinking; they were almost like collaborators. For example one guy shared my delusion of undercover work. Another believed he was turning into a werewolf. A Christian girl I knew performed some kind of exorcism ceremony, chanting in Hebrew, to drive out demons. I also hitched a lift with a Polish man, again a Christian, who believed that the Second Coming was nigh and that those who hadn't surrendered to Jesus would be condemned to hell. I remember once on a psychiatric ward I met a red-headed girl dressed in combats. We went for a drink together and in my deluded state I imagined she was a key secret agent in this good vs evil war with a message for me. I recall we sat in a pub, both of us asking God for protection from the devil, with her asking if she or I were an angel. I never entertained this belief that I was an angel, but my psychotic thinking did turn a corner there, with me believing that angels were amongst us masquerading as humans. I began to believe mankind was on the cusp of a new age of purity, love, compassion, understanding, higher knowledge and spiritual awareness. I believed that the angels were here to lead the way and guide us into this new level of existence.

This three-month manic high came crashing down around me and I sank into a dark depression, a world of hopeless despair with no meaning whatsoever, punctuated by thoughts of suicide. Somehow I eventually managed to claw my way out of this hole, and thankfully total psychosis has not been with me for four months now.

Becky

It takes time to put the jigsaw pieces back when recovering from a deep psychotic episode.

Reality seems to get all mixed-up and confused; working out what has been real and what has not been real is the hard part.

The Psychiatrist
&
The Psychologist

The first visit to a psychiatrist is generally a very scary occasion—remember, at this stage most sufferers think they are alone and imagine that their symptoms are unique to them. What seems to happen is that, after a brief chat, an antidepressant is usually dished out, or some other medication. Then it is a very long time before the next appointment. But once they have begun, most patients feel the need to talk very regularly to somebody who understands, and this process is denied them.

A psychologist is very different to a psychiatrist and it is important to make this distinction. A psychiatrist has medical training and will see a mental health difficulty as a disorder and something that needs treatment through, usually, medication. A psychologist does not have medical training and they are trained instead in psychology and clinical psychology, or psychotherapy, and will help through a variety of talking treatments.

Becky

Every psychiatrist I have ever seen has only ever treated the symptoms of my distress. Eventually I got to see a psychologist who treated the cause. It is a combination of them both that has helped me to get to where I am today. I wish I had received the attention of a psychologist at the beginning of my treatment, nearly 15 years ago, as I don't think I would still be using the mental health services today.

Receiving that label

Receiving a label, or getting a diagnosis, affects people in different ways. Some hate having a label hung around their neck while others welcome recognition of symptoms. The important thing to remember is that no diagnosis is set in stone. Some of us have several diagnoses during the course of our mental health history. Indeed, different psychiatrists will often offer widely different points of view.

Becky

I didn't receive my diagnosis for a long time. At first it was 'clinical depression with panic disorder' and then over the years it changed from diagnosis to diagnosis, all varying in degree, some seemingly worse than others.

Not knowing what was wrong was the hardest bit. The never-ending wait to be told 'you're MAD!!' I knew I wasn't ill, I was just struggling with life, but soon that was washed away by the tablets and the side-effects and the stigma. Receiving a diagnosis was receiving a label, which meant that everyone knew I couldn't cope. It didn't help that the label kept changing, and the view society then had of me made it a hundred times worse. I already *felt* different and being labelled as such just compounded that feeling of difference and isolation.

I had gone from having my own home, a life, some friends and a future, to having less than nothing. The few friends I had could not cope with my changing moods, my bizarre behaviour and thoughts, and slowly one by one they disappeared. I had to leave my flat and move back to my parents, eventually being admitted to hospital. My future career as a teacher was gone. If all this happened to you in the space of a few weeks, even without difficulties, how would you cope?

Chris

There was no diagnosis given after my first brief stay in hospital. That came a month or so later when I was admitted to QMC in Nottingham as a voluntary patient.

My initial diagnosis was 'episodic psychotic', which a few days later changed to 'psychotic'. About a week later the diagnosis 'bipolar' was given. I think at the time I had mixed feelings about having a diagnosis. I mean, primarily, it is a lot to accept that you are mentally ill, with all the connotations, the initial feelings of shame, and the stigma. At the same time I had no knowledge of manic depression and so had minimal insight into the condition I had been told I had. So really, during the time I was in hospital, I had little or no understanding of my situation. Ultimately though, receiving this diagnosis I suppose helped as it gave me an urge to read the literature about the condition.

A year after my initial diagnosis I have in an indirect way (I mean without consultation) been informed that my condition is suspected to be mainly 'psychotic bipolar' or 'schizo-affective disorder' (no regard for my extended periods of depression). Having received this indefinite and somewhat inaccurate diagnosis I have come to the realisation that the best person to understand my condition is—me. I accept that I have had psychotic episodes with delusions, hallucinations, mistaken beliefs, confusion and fear etc. I also recognise that I have had some periods of depression, and that my condition is pretty episodic with periods of relative good health in between. That's it, really. Why complicate it more? I don't want to be pigeon-holed as x or y or z and I realise there is a lot of overlap between schizophrenia (x) and manic depression (y) and schizo-affective disorder (z). Anyone with diagnosis y or z could in fact also exhibit some symptoms of x. Is anyone mainly y or z?

Hugh

The psychiatrist diagnosed 'manic depression'. Personally I was delighted to receive a diagnosis. I needed a label for my bewildering illness which, for me, was deep troughs of depression followed by short bursts of hyperactivity. I could now identify what I had got, plus my GP had retired and the new one was much more aware of psychiatric problems.

Anon

I didn't find out what my diagnosis was until much later on in my illness. My precise diagnosis was 'schizo-affective disorder'. I'm unclear why this is different to schizophrenia. The doctor has explained it many times but I still can't suss it out. The medication is the same. I'm totally indifferent to the technicalities—what matters is that the voices and the hallucinations are kept at bay.

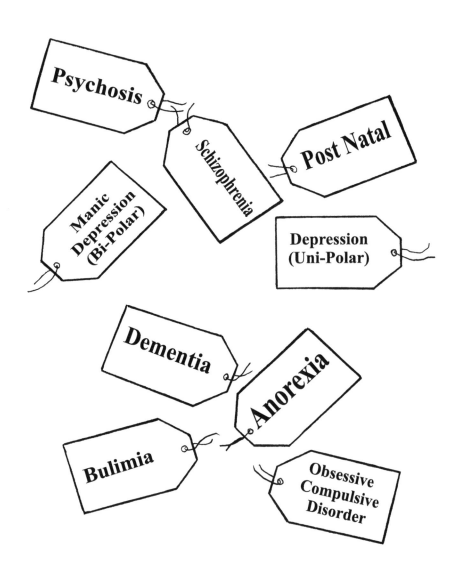

So you have a diagnosis

Some of us welcome receiving a diagnosis because it confirms the symptoms are real. Others hate it because it is like a large label round their necks. A common trait is that diagnoses change over the years, which just goes to show *how very little still is known about mental health distress.*

There is a book of all the diagnoses that can be given to someone experiencing mental health difficulties. This book is called the DSM, the *Diagnostic Statistical Manual*, currently at the fourth edition. Each diagnosis has a list of criteria of which a significant number must be met before a diagnosis is given. The problem here is when you fit more than one of the diagnoses, which is because many of the criteria overlap. We are all individuals and it is very difficult, if not impossible, to lump groups of people with very different histories and experiences and difficulties into one box. The *Diagnostic Statistical Manual* is now being rewritten and even more diagnoses are being created.

Becky

I would prefer to see someone receive a personal and individual description of their difficulties and their history instead of a diagnosis. Psychologists do this and they call it a *formulation* and it is basically a description of where a person has come from, what has been of help in the past, their difficulties and their strengths as well as the identified areas that they want to work on.

Medication

Medication can be a huge bone of contention. Usually, on first contact, the GP will probably prescribe some antidepressants, but when forwarded to a psychiatrist s/he may prescribe totally different medication. Medication is a very individual thing. The same drug will affect different people in different ways, acting as it does on the chemicals in the brain and causing many physical side effects.

Those of us who have a long mental health history will have tried several and probably many drugs over our lives, indeed so many that it is difficult to remember them all. It would be hard to determine which medication worked best. The service user really has to place his/her trust in the hands of the psychiatrist. Some patients decide to try and stop taking their medication off their own bat, usually because of side effects. However, without support and steady withdrawal this can be dangerous.

Ann

I should think I have tried nearly every antidepressant going, some for only two or three weeks because they didn't suit me. They were either making me feel high (couldn't relax) or the side effects were so bad I couldn't cope with them. Seven years ago, the last time I was in hospital, it was agreed I should try Lithium. So I took Lithium as a stabiliser and Venlafaxine as an antidepressant and Thiridozine to help me sleep. Thiridozine was then taken off the market and I had to change the Venlafaxine for Dothiepin for sleep and for an anti-depressant.

The friend I made 18 years ago became my hero/idol. She had a long history of depression and it took many years to stabilise her. Manic depression was her diagnosis. I had known her for about a year before they were able to stabilise her using about four different medications. Lithium and Carbomazapine were two of them. She took her medicines without complaint and observed the rules with them i.e. no alcohol, wearing a hat in the sun, using strong sun factor etc. When her mother died and she herself became very ill with arthritis and psoriasis, she kept going in her cheerful, cheeky way. She was always willing to do anything to help anyone if it was within her power.

Anon

Once, when I was in hospital, they watched while I took their medications, which was just as well as otherwise I wouldn't have taken them since up to that point I thought they weren't what they said they were. I was given two types of pill. One was for the depression and one for the psychosis. A few days after I'd been admitted, the psychosis went away. This was a great relief as it had been with me for a year. It also restored my faith in the doctor's abilities to treat me.

The antidepressants were less effective and although they did give a slight improvement (I know this from the fact that when I stopped taking them I felt terrible) I still feel depressed to this day. I think it is part of my personality.

Hugh

Yes, I do receive medication. I am on Lithium, Venlafaxine and Chlorpromazine. I have been on countless different types of medication over the years and it has always been difficult to tell which works and which doesn't. My present combination keeps my mood more or less stable but I still get depressed from time to time. I suppose it does prevent the huge lows I used to get but it also knocks off the highs which I used to love and which made the deep lows more bearable. There is no doubt that I need to be on psychiatric medication but it does somewhat control my life. I get very tired and this limits what I can and can't do.

Becky

Urghhh! I hate my medication. Don't get me wrong, it can help some people and it helps take the edge of my distress at times, but the other effects that it has are not good.

I take antidepressants, antipsychotics, sedatives, sleeping tablets and a range of medication for my physical health. I am addicted emotionally and physically to the sedatives and sleeping tablets. I am on the highest dose of antidepressants and normally you should be an inpatient to receive this dosage and be monitored; I am neither.

The effects of the antipsychotics, when I have been on higher doses, have been distressing in themselves. They have numbed me down so much I can't think at all even to make a cup of tea. The agitation and constant moving attracts the stares of other people and the aching intensity in the joints that I get, even on the lower doses, is horrible. Then there is the constant salivation and the soaking wet pillow every morning and the vivid nightmares and dreams.

I have had other physical effects as well, such as high blood pressure and life-threatening reactions to one drug I was given. My head and muscles contracted, going into spasms and requiring emergency admission and treatment. Then there are the mood changes that became so apparent on one drug that I had to come off it, taking months for me to return to my usual self. Oh, and there are the withdrawal effects if I come off *any* of the drugs, which again takes months, if not years, to right itself. To this day I still have to take one

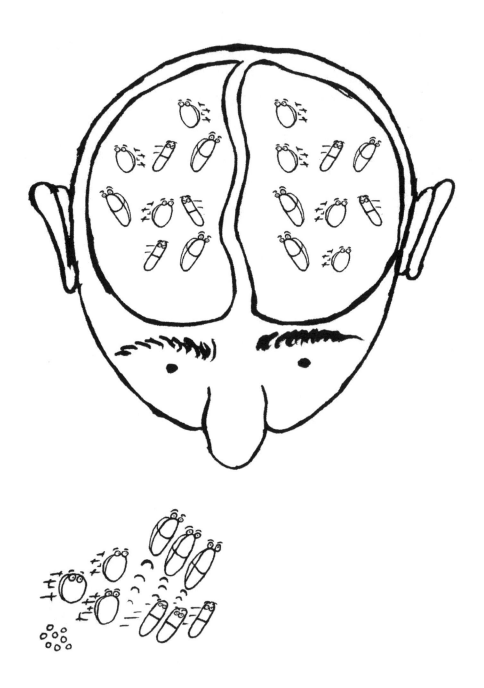

such drug because I can't seem to withdraw from it at all without becoming acutely ill during the withdrawal process, no matter how slowly I do it.

For me the effects of the medications that are positive are very limited and are mostly concerned with helping me get enough sleep. They have also come in handy when I have wanted to take an overdose, and maybe that's the best I can say for them! Certainly the distressing effects far outweigh the positive.

Chris

While on the ward I was given 20 mg of the antipsychotic Olanzapine, which seems to be the preferred medication of choice for psychotics in Nottingham. The meds were dished out at 10 pm every night and I knew that within one hour I would be incapacitated and almost unable to move. I was on this dosage for one month on the ward and at my point of discharge was still quite manic. Side effects of this medication included muscular cramps in my neck, throat and tongue. I couldn't talk properly, my tongue felt swollen and my head was locked in various painful positions. I was prescribed Procyclidine to counteract the muscle problems, but this drug caused blurred vision, which was unexpected and frightening. I was offered another drug to counteract this side effect, but I could see a domino effect building and so decided to quit taking Procyclidine and just put up with the locked neck. Fortunately these side effects vanished. Olanzapine did help me to sleep at regular times but it didn't help to alleviate my symptoms of psychosis.

Eventually, after discharge, I managed to get my meds changed to a mood stabilizer, Sodium Valporate Depakote. When my mania passed I had another period of depression which lasted about six months. I was desperate for help with this but could not be prescribed anti-depressants as they have a tendency to trigger mania. Sodium Valporate didn't help me at all with my depression and Olanzapine probably only worsened it, draining me of energy and motivation. The sedative effects of this drug made it very difficult for me to get up in the mornings and sometimes I would lie in bed till two or three in the afternoon.

 After further meetings with my psychiatrist I managed to get my meds changed to Lamotragine, another mood stabilizer, but with anti-depressant effects. I thought I had finally found a drug that could help me and so this gave me some hope. Although this medication can cause hallucinations, aggression, irritability and confusion and also binds to melanin in the iris of the eye (the long-term effects of which are unknown) it is the medication I am remaining on for the time being. On balance I want stability and hate depression and if this drug can help me with this then I am prepared to take it.

The medication minefield

We have all been on a huge mixture of medication over the years. Far too often it seems that the prescription is a lottery. Try this, and if that doesn't work, try that. Some psychiatrists have favourite medications that they always prescribe. Some of us have found a combination of medication that seems to work, but others are still chopping and changing after many years and never seem to find one that really works for them.

Becky

My psychiatrist told me that *I* needed to help the medication to work and I asked what I needed to do. Surely a medication either works or it doesn't? It can't be my fault!

It is very scary how the medication that we have all been prescribed, works. Antidepressants should be prescribed only on a short-term basis but many are on them for life. Antipsychotics are prescribed many times over the recommended dosage. This is now slowly being addressed and medication is starting to be seen as the last port of call.

However, it is hard to withdraw from medication that has affected the neurons in the brain and has many side effects and withdrawal effects. There are both mental and physical difficulties that arise from taking or withdrawing from the medication given. Valium, a benzodiazepine, is highly addictive but frequently prescribed.

It is my belief, and that of most others in our support group, that 'talking therapies' are as effective as, or more effective than, medication, and more and more research evidence is accumulating to support this view.

Richard Toon, *Phoenix Rising*, Mixed Media

Mental Health Services

There are plenty of services around if you ask the right questions, but you certainly cannot always rely on the information being divulged automatically. Services include psychiatrists, psychologists, social workers, community psychiatric nurses, occupational therapists and of course mental health wards in the hospitals. I used to live in a small town where it was difficult to find services, but since moving to a city I have found there are a lot more available.

Ann

I saw a psychotherapist for a year after the first stay in hospital. My goodness me, how my eyes were opened! Some of what we talked about took a while to be proved or believed. Now when I have a low period it helps to remember what we talked about i.e. nothing is perfect. I might do things differently from someone else, but it is my way and it works for me, just as their way works for them.

When I was in my teens, if I had a problem or was upset I would volunteer to help with the washing up. It would take me as long as getting to the last pot before I would find the courage to say anything. The psychotherapist asked me, if my children were upset, would I want to know? I replied 'yes'. So the therapist asked me why I thought my mother would not have wanted to know or help me if I was unhappy. Today I try to be aware of my family's moods and ask if I think there is a problem. They don't always tell me and I don't always detect their moods correctly, but then I am not perfect, nobody is perfect and nothing is perfect, not even nature.

I learnt that I was very good at some things and hopeless at others and this is the same for everybody. I would check my sons' school bags at least once a week as sometimes they would need something special for school. Another mum told me she wished she'd known their child had to produce that special something for school (she worked full-time) as she did not have the time that I did to check. We cannot be everything to everyone or do everything ourselves.

I learned to love myself for who I am, warts and all. It's not what's on the outside; it's the inner person that's important. I learned to question negative thoughts.

Becky

I have received some services from the mental health system that have been good. When I finally received the services of a psychologist and supportive community nurse, things started to change. *I was heard for the first time in my life*. I could talk openly to the psychologist about the distress and the voices. It was then that I started to move forward. It was the sort of help I needed. The community nurse listened to me as an equal human being, giving me back control over my own life. He believed I could achieve what I wanted to achieve in life and he saw my potential. He saw a future for me and had hope.

Along the way I have met other like-minded individuals who have also seen me as a person in my own right, but they have been few and far between. I must mention, however, one nurse who was an inspiration to me. He described me as 'wonderfully strange'. But it wasn't this statement that changed my life. It was something else he said. The nurse asked me, 'What do you want out of life? What are your dreams?' At first I said I had none, that they had been taken away from me, but then I thought more and more about what I had wanted before I got ill. He then said, 'Why not follow those dreams?'

'WHY NOT?' I came up with lots of excuses, like I could no longer work with children because of the label I had received, but the phrase 'why not?' kept coming back to me. Why couldn't I do the things I wanted to do? Why couldn't I have dreams? And why couldn't I follow them? Just like anybody else I needed to have dreams to follow, a purpose and a reason to live. From the day he put the idea into my head I started to follow my dreams again, changing my life completely!!

Most of my experience of the mental health services, though, have been poor. The services took away my autonomy and the control I had over my life. Instead they controlled my life for me. The treatment I received in hospital was not one of being cared for and supported, but of risk management and control and medication enforcement. The psychiatrists similarly only saw life from their point of view and they needed to be in control. I, as a person, was not heard most of the time, what I needed or wanted. Discussions were one-way and involvement in my own care was at best tokenistic and at worst nonexistent. I was labelled and put in a box and if I argued with them, or tried to debate with them about my care, I was labelled as attention-seeking or as having a personality disorder. I was the lowest of the low, I did not matter.

Anon

The support I've had since entering the hospital has been very good. The staff are always helpful but I sometimes wonder if there is really anything they can do for me. They may be trained professionals but they still have no magic wand or answers to all the questions. I have to say, I have had more support than I expected. I'm not very demanding of them because I don't know what they could do. In the end it seems to me you are on your own.

51

Hugh

Because I have been involved with mental health services for so long I can say that the support I have received has been a mixed bag. There have been psychiatrists I have had a good relationship with and others whom I have not. Personally I have found that having a good relationship with one's psychiatrist is essential for a state of wellbeing. Some CPNs (community psychiatric nurses) have been excellent, whereas others have only been adequate.

On the whole the support has been what I have needed, although often the time taken to get hold of somebody is way too long.

Chris

My key worker helped me with filling in my DLA (Disability Living Allowance) form and also assisted me by contacting the council about my homeless situation and need of accommodation. This helped, as when a flat became available my name was still fresh in the council's mind. My key worker also referred me to the Open Door project and advised me how to contact the Rushcliffe Mental Health Support Group, which helped.

My criticism is their reluctance to arrange some kind of talking therapy for me which would have really helped me during my depression, but my consultant psychiatrist advised against it as he believed it would be "too painful". . . and probably too costly.

So where—and what kind?

Availability is patchy. If you are lucky you can gain access to the relevant mental health services for yourself. But you have always got to ask and sometimes fight for the service that you need. It would be great if information about mental health services was more widely available. It is generally agreed that access to a psychologist, rather than a psychiatrist, is very beneficial, but it is hard to access and there are long waiting times, months and sometimes years.

Hospital

Most of us have spent some time in hospital. For some it can be a very helpful process, for others a very anxious and disturbing time. A common perception is that the staff on the wards are not as caring as they should be. Whether this is due to lack of time is unknown. One thing that is very important is that the patient has plenty of visitors because this helps continue the contact with the outside world.

Ann

I spent four weeks on an acute psychiatric ward. Surprisingly and amazingly, you couldn't tell who the patients were and who were staff, as patients were asked to dress during the day and staff didn't wear uniform. At first I couldn't work out why someone was following me around all the time. Then one of the nurses explained that she would be observing me for the next hour. "Why?" I asked. The answer was that they didn't want me to attempt suicide again, so I was on what was called close obs (observations).

When I met the psychiatrist for the first time I didn't know what to say to him. He suggested that I wrote down my troubles (I feel sure, looking back, that he must have regretted suggesting this because I wrote reams and reams and reams). My second experience of a psychiatrist was very different and much better.

My diagnosis was 'depression', and although I didn't want to take medication (it was never forced upon me), eventually I agreed to take it because I was not feeling much better. I wasn't eating or sleeping very well (everything tasted like cardboard). What a relief it was, chatting to the other patients and discovering that I was not the only one who had taken an overdose, or the only person suffering from depression.

I made very good friends with one of the other patients. We have seen each other at least once a week for the last 18 years. Sadly, she died not so long ago.

Not only did I write down thoughts, I also talked to the nurses on the ward, two of whom were particularly helpful. I was discharged from hospital into the care of a psychotherapist. It was very frightening going home and I wasn't at all sure how or if I would cope.

I have had two more stays in hospital and these partly contributed to the decision to try Lithium. I have never been sectioned.

Chris

The first time I was ever admitted to hospital with mental distress I was sectioned but released after four days. On the second occasion I went in as a voluntary patient but would have been sectioned had I not volunteered. I recall a discussion on the assessment ward with a junior psychiatrist three days after admittance. I wanted out, I felt trapped, restricted, like my freedom had been taken away. I was told that if I wanted to leave I would be sectioned and so I resigned myself to staying there.

I was visited nightly by my father and was eventually allowed escorted-leave with him. I got on pretty well with fellow patients. The thing lacking on the treatment ward was some kind of treatment besides medication. I think I really needed a health professional to talk with, either a psychologist or cognitive therapist, or a counsellor of some description, but I gather that this kind of treatment is too costly for the NHS, which receives budget cuts every year. Some books or documentaries on mental health recovery would also have been of value. Occupational therapy was a bit of a joke really, not stimulating enough and sometimes patronising, although we had one day-trip in a month to Attenborough Nature Reserve, and relaxation sessions were helpful. Access to a swimming pool and gym would have been excellent and would have allowed patients to release some tension and could have helped reduce anxiety or depression. Someone who is manic and has excessive energy is hardly going to 'burn it off' sitting on a ward all day long without any exercise. On a positive note I did manage to get hold of some art materials while on the ward, so that gave me something to do along with listening to music, writing and socialising with others on the ward.

The thing about the ward environment that stood out for me was a group of people who used to sit in a line, staring straight ahead at nothing, obviously heavily medicated. Additionally there were those that were quite institutionalised, having been on the wards for years. One oldish guy I met had the door to his flat bashed down by police one night, was put on a section and forcibly medicated. This was apparently for not complying with instructions to take his meds. When I came off the ward about a year ago he was also close to discharge. I visited a friend on the ward about a week ago and sadly I saw this chap sitting on the floor outside the hospital, smoking, wearing the same clothes he had on a year ago and no doubt back in the same boat.

QMC psychiatric wards to me are low stimulus, tedious places where time drags and you just want out. At least it would have been like that had it not been for friends in the same situation. The lowest levels of staff are underpaid and there are too few of them to allow any time for one-to-one talks with patients who need to talk. Treatment seems to revolve around medication. While there I described the situation as like putting a band-aid on a black hole. TREATMENT WARD? I don't think so. I think many of the nursing staff working on QMC psychiatric wards are demoralized and have very little hope of understanding or helping the seriously mentally ill, let alone curing them. I suppose they are, though, a safe haven for distressed people where you will not be judged or made to feel odd for your behaviour.

One problem, which could easily be remedied, is quiet areas. These are where visitors can spend time with loved ones on the ward in comfort and privacy, without disturbance from patients on high observation or interference from nursing staff. But they don't exist. WHY NOT? Also, visiting times during the week are too restrictive.

Hugh

The first time I went into hospital, back in 1969, was a real shock to the system. I felt absolutely wretched on the ward and couldn't wait to get home again. I don't believe the experience did me any good whatsoever.

The second time was much more recent, 1998, and I didn't think it was appropriate for me to go to hospital although I didn't argue with the advice I was given. Once again I couldn't wait to get home.

Anon

Hospital was not as bad as I thought it would be. The nurses were very empathising. At the time I thought, due to my psychosis, that the whole thing was an act and that they were institutionalising me and would keep me there as long as they could.

They didn't tell me I was under observation and it was strange having someone come and look at you at regular intervals and not know why. Not being allowed out, I started to feel like a prisoner, but it was all right once the nurse took me for a walk.

Becky

My first admission into hospital was a so-called voluntary admission. Basically I either went in voluntarily or I was sectioned and forced onto the ward. (Where was the voluntary bit, you ask? I still question that.)

Again, questions ruled my head. What do I take? Will everyone be like me? What will patients and staff be like? Will I be safe? Will I share a room? What will the therapy be?

Walking down that corridor was long, a void, a tunnel down to the unknown. I had my parents on both sides guiding me as I walked. Places had become unreal and finding my direction was hard. I felt consumed by emotion. I didn't want to be here, I wanted to die, but then I wasn't here for me, I was here for my family and their concern.

Dying, for me, at this point would have been a relief and an escape from the depths of despair. Depression is not the Monday blues or feeling a little down. No, this was 'there is no way out'. That tunnel with the light at the end that people talk about—it had no light, and I had fallen into a deep pit that had caved in every time I had tried to climb out, until I no longer tried. But the place at the end of this corridor was my only hope that my parents would feel I had done my best, and that I would be safe. They had found me self-harming again, something they still do not understand. I needed the self-harm to relieve the distress, to continue to survive—not to die. The voices I heard that others couldn't, they were my sanctuary. At times the voices were distressing, though, and confused even further my thoughts and anxieties.

Panic ran through my body when I saw the door, I didn't want to go in. The staff were expecting me, though, and ushered me into the entrance room where I sat and waited. The panic would not go away and I started to hyperventilate, breathing more and more quickly, my heart pounding through my chest, about to burst. I have had panic attacks many times before and even though I know I am not going to die and that it will eventually fade away, it felt like this every time it happened.

I was taken into a small room and interviewed for what seemed hours, although apparently it was only 20 minutes. I was asked about my self-harm and the voices and any other difficulties I was experiencing, but I was not in a fit state physically or emotionally to express myself clearly.

It took me days to work out where everything was, including the toilet and where to go to get a drink of tea. I relied heavily on other patients for information—that is, when I could eventually talk to other patients. I was told little by the nurses and weeks passed before I even knew I could be escorted by my parents off the ward for a walk. Going for a walk was an invaluable respite from the ward, even though the car parks I walked on became dull and tiresome.

The view from the window of the room I was in was of those same car parks and I began to pass the time observing the regular visitors and staff that came and left with their cars, wishing I could go with them. I was so bored at times and so tired at other times. The main focus of the day was mealtimes, with little else to do. The therapy I needed, *that person to talk to*, did not exist.

The only thing I did get was constant observation and drugs—endless drugs. These drugs were even more intense than before and made me feel worse than I had when I was first admitted. The nurses said the effects would wear off and that I would get used to them, but I didn't. I felt like my legs were weighted down and they would not go in the direction I wanted. The agitation intensified and I needed to keep moving, even if it meant I walked up and down the small ward most of the day. My vision blurred and I felt intolerably nauseous for most of the time. When I did sit, I clock-watched. Minutes and seconds passed slowly and time seemed to drag ever more slowly with the passing of the days and weeks.

I left that ward still with my anxiety, depression and hallucinations but so drugged to the eyeballs that I could not think about them and did not care. I had been medicated so much I had become a different person—a quiet, subdued and easily manipulated person. Was it the effect of the drugs or the effect of being locked away for so long from everything that was familiar and real? I no longer knew what I wanted or needed from life, it was all one long, big blur and all I wanted to do was sleep in my own bed, stroke my own dog and be somewhere I felt safe.

Had I left with post-traumatic stress disorder? Probably. Had the ward helped me reach the cause of my distress and help me overcome it? No. It had ignored the problem, drugged the symptoms and caused me to fear ever going on the ward again, so ultimately causing more problems than it solved.

'The doctors are always right. They know what they are doing,' I told myself. 'You have to get worse before you get better,' the psychiatrists explained, and I foolishly believed them. I am stronger now and I am more confident and able to stand up for what I believe, but it has taken me ten years to become 'me' again. It took me six of those years to fight to see a psychologist and at the same time receive help for physical health needs that had been ignored by going to a private hospital. All in all it was me who knew what I needed, right from the beginning—someone to talk to, believe in me and support me through the past distress. If only I had been listened to back then instead of their using mix after mix of chemicals that simply subdued me!

Some get benefit, others . . .
Some of us get benefit from being in hospital. Others hate every minute. Hospital wards are very tedious and very busy places and

there are supposed to be plenty of therapies, but this is usually limited to pottery. One would think that being on an acute ward there would be plenty of access to doctors and nurses, but this is just not the case. Trying to find someone just to talk to is hard, and usually the only people who take the time to listen are the other patients who are with you on the ward.

What would I say to someone who thinks they might have a mental health difficulty?

o First I would let them know they're not mad; a lot of people are going through, and have been through, similar difficulties

o Then I would listen to the person and what they want to say and learn about them before making any suggestions or giving ideas.

o Possible ideas, though, could be writing down thoughts and feelings in a diary, on bits of paper or through poetry or art.

o Find a peer group or someone they trust who has been through, or is going through, difficulties.

o Make them aware of their options for support—GP, Counsellor, mental health services, medication, complementary therapies, support groups.

But most of all let them know—
help is out there and that they are not alone and that people do recover.

Richard Toon, *Critters*, Mixed Media

Peer Support

Peer literally means an equal. A peer is someone who has similar age, history or experience to you. Peer groups fall naturally together.

How our peer support group works.

We meet once a week for two hours in a local pub. We find that the relaxed atmosphere this generates helps the group to function efficiently. When people are ill they sometimes find it hard to attend, but if they do manage to they are met warmly by the group members. Often, attending when not at your best can help bring a sense of achievement.

Apart from supporting each other at the weekly meeting, the group also organises social activities. A few years ago we had a holiday in Scotland. Last year we ventured further afield, to Turkey. We go to Cornwall every year and last year we even went camping and canoeing in Derbyshire. We go to local sites of interest and arrange theatre and cinema trips. Having such a full and varied social programme gives us all something to look forward to.

There is a big difference between our group and other groups such as AA (Alcoholics Anonymous) and DA (Depressives Anonymous) in that we are much more informal. Some groups forbid members from meeting outside the group or even exchanging numbers. This is something we decided not to do. We meet socially all the time and share our phone numbers with whoever we wish. Another difference is that our group is run *by* its members *for* its members. No professionals are involved apart from the occasional courtesy call. We even meet up outside the group meetings.

All of us in our support group view the group's support as of paramount importance. The support of peers can often be more important and valuable than the mental health services, including psychiatrists.

Peers can sympathise and empathise with what you are going through. They can offer advice gained from personal experience. They can offer a valuable sounding board when all you want to do is talk. It can give you really good friends who will stick by you through thick and thin.

Becky

I started the support group because I felt so lonely with the experiences I had had on the acute ward and the difficulties I was experiencing at the time. From talking with the people I had met on the ward, I knew I could not be alone in feeling this way. I felt isolated. Peer support had helped me on the ward and I wondered if it could help me in the community as well. I needed to talk with people who had more awareness of what I had been through and the distress I was experiencing.

The group has been running for twelve years now and I have gained more from the group than I have probably given. It has at times kept me out of hospital, kept me from relapsing and supported me from week to week. Knowing you are talking with someone who knows and experiences similar distress is comforting and I can feel safe and secure in talking openly. I have also gained from the knowledge that people have learnt about what helps them cope. The group also arranges social activities and this gives us something to look forward to doing together. The support is two-way and this cannot be given by mental health service providers, no matter how much they want to.

The support group has been essential in my recovery and rediscovery. The group has no professional running it. We are all peers and we support each other. We run the group—some of us more than others, but everyone has a say in how and what we do. Through the group I have learnt to try out things such as the coping strategies that have helped other people. So it creates an opportunity to look at the world differently and they always say a problem shared is a problem halved. It is also a social group and I have tried things that I could never do on my own and even if I could, would never try due to my anxieties and fears; but as a group we are so much stronger. We have met every week, been on outings and even been on holiday. I haven't the strength yet to do this on my own but I am not alone. This is one thing the group has shown me, that I am not alone in my struggles and my fight to survive.

Anon 2 wanted to write a piece for the group to go in the book. We thought it would be nice to include it in this section.

Anon 2

I'd been on drugs until September 2006. In November of that year my mind threw up some very strong feelings that I'd not had for about four years. Up until that point I had been doing some voluntary work and trying therapy. Although the work was important in pinpointing what kind of person I was, it was no longer beneficial to my health. My guess is that the drugs had worn off. I stopped taking the drugs because the side effects were too much to bear. I decided to quit therapy as I thought it would have similar effects on my health. I had a strong urge to socialise but also knew that if I did there would be ramifications which would need to be dealt with, otherwise my physical health could suffer. My therapist gave me a book of self-help groups. I chose the Rushcliffe Mental Health Support Group because I wanted to socialise with real people, not healthcare workers, and I didn't like the statements made by the other self-help groups. Although NHS therapeutic activities have benefited me, I eventually found them too restrictive and stopped using them.

When I joined the group they were meeting in a pub, which was cool because I went to pubs before becoming ill, but it did take some getting used to. The environment of the group clarified my feelings about what I wanted to do with my life and it certainly felt good to have some half-decent conversations in a pub setting and not just be sitting there twiddling my thumbs. Attending the group gave me the confidence that I could socialise and deal with the ramifications.

After joining the group I applied for some part-time paid work which I had not done since April 2006. Because of the way the group is run there is no pressure to attend every meeting, which means it fits in with my lifestyle. As the group members respect my wishes there is also no pressure to join in the numerous activities the group organises. A group member also kindly invited me to their home for Christmas, without which I would have been pretty bored and possibly lonely. It had been a while since I'd been round to someone's house so it was good to know I could cope with being out and about.

I now socialise outside of the group, doing activities that should increase my mental fitness even further. As I gain in knowledge I am more and more enabled to cope with a greater variety of situations. I'm not sure if I'll attend the group in the future but it's nice to know it's there if I want it. As one of the group members has an email address I can contact them without incurring any costs. I hope that when meeting other people they can see the merits of the life I lead.

Benefits of peer support

It is generally agreed between us that peer support really is vital. Obviously we are biased, as the Rushcliffe Mental Health Support

Group is our baby, but we all agree that we have gained tremendous benefits from it. Fellow members are always there to support and the activities we organize are a welcome release from spending so much time on our own.

Corinne Smith, *Hidden Strand*, Charcoal

Coping

We all cope in different ways. Some of us rely completely on medication; others get support and help from a self-help group. Some people cope through keeping themselves really busy, by getting involved in courses, groups, training and meetings. Some rely on their own mental history to put life into perspective. There is no easy solution and for those of us who have suffered a long time we have probably tried various options.

Ann

I cope on a day to day basis.

I'm not very good about getting up in the morning. When I'm OK, it helps to set myself jobs to do the next day. I may not get half of them done, but at least if I have done some I can say to myself, "Well, I haven't done nothing." Sometimes I find if I get going and keep going I achieve quite a lot and amaze myself.

We need to give ourselves a pat on the back sometimes. Everybody has good days and bad days. I have to remind myself that I am doing the job my way and that's OK.

Many of us are too hard on ourselves, becoming the judge, the jury and executioner. Try to think how you might judge someone else, especially another mental health sufferer, and then apply that judgement to yourself.

I am a carer (for my son) as well as a sufferer. Christopher is at university now, but the last ten years have not been easy for him. He is academically gifted but has always hated school. Good GCSE results helped him enjoy his 6th form. He is the type of person who needs to play and rest as well as work (his brother had to work hard to get to university and so Christopher would sometimes feel guilty because he didn't have to work so hard). When he has a bout of depression I try to chat with him. I will take him a cup of tea and make myself available to him for at least half an hour. Eventually he will open up.

I tell him, so long as he gets up and gets dressed, I don't mind what he does for the rest of the day, whether he watches TV, does a jigsaw puzzle etc. Just so long as he rests. I tell him if he had a broken leg or arm or a bad cold he would rest in order to heal. Well, mental health is just another illness.

Resting is important. This last ten years or so I try to see when it's important not to do anything other than have a bath, watch telly, read a good book etc. The washing-up and everything else can wait until tomorrow. If I get too involved in something in the evening, I usually can't sleep very well. This is not good because I have not recharged my batteries to cope with the next day.

Becky

One of my main coping strategies is checking things out with other people that I trust. I hear a lot of things that other people don't and get paranoid on a daily basis. If I can check this out with other people, what is real and what is not, whether I am being paranoid or not, if I trust that they will tell me the truth, then I know what is really happening in my life. If I don't do this, my paranoia and the voices get stronger and spiral out of control until I hit a major crisis.

72

Johanna Sharland, *Pastel Thoughts*, Pastels, Pen & Acetate

Another coping strategy is to take respite from my life, either for a day or a week. This could be at home or away. The up side to having this respite is that I can do more at other times because I feel stronger.

Walking the dog or going for a bike ride sometimes works, depending on how tired I am.

Relaxation techniques I learnt through a day centre and through my yoga also mostly let me escape from my thoughts, and clear my head.

Listening to Talking Books, hoovering, cleaning, singing to myself, all helps to limit the hallucinations, at least some of the time.

Of course all these things only work to a certain extent and there are some days that just staying in bed for half a day, and sometimes the whole day, is the only way I can cope with life, limiting the amount of stimuli around me.

Hugh

My first means of coping is the simple act of getting out of bed. This simple act leads to facing the day each day. I know when I have been deeply depressed this easy act can take on huge proportions. Many a time I have spent the day in bed, unwilling or unable to face the world. So getting up in the morning at a reasonable time is vitally important.

Secondly, keeping a written account of all the things I have planned helps me organise. I make a list of all the things I want to do and tick them off when they have been done. This gives me a firm focus to my life and I find it very useful. When I stop doing this and have nothing planned, then my life falls into disarray. When the writing stops, then it is time to start worrying.

Allied to this last point, I try to have as many activities, groups, meetings and outings arranged as possible. When I start losing interest, cancelling or simply not turning up, it is a sign I am withdrawing into myself. It is important to keep contact with friends and family.

Anon

My main coping strategies are to get plenty of sleep (something I wasn't doing when I was working and studying). I also eat well and go for plenty of walks.

When dealing with severe distress and anxiety about something coming up, I have no choice but to force myself to do whatever I have to, whether it be going to the shops or meeting some people. I don't believe there is much people can do to help, except reassure.

A variety of strategies

Between us we have a number of different coping strategies. Getting up at a reasonable time in the morning is very common. Keeping in touch regularly with friends is seen as very helpful. Another key element is to keep as busy as you can but without overdoing it. Something that helps some people is to write everything down. This includes plans and also what has been achieved.

Be patient

by Ann

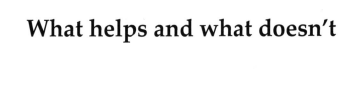

What helps and what doesn't

As always, different people have different ideas about what helps and is useful, and what doesn't help when we are struggling with our illness. All of us are agreed that what helps us immensely is our mental health support group. It is a safe haven to come to regularly every week to meet friends, support one another and arrange social activities. Personally I find writing things down helps a lot. I plan ahead and write everything down and tick things off when they are done. Keeping busy is another thing that helps a lot. Having good friends to confide in is also extremely useful.

What DOES NOT help is having people say to you 'pull yourself together' or 'snap out of it'. Also, often waiting a long time, sometimes months, even years, for an appointment to see a psychologist or another worker can be distressing.

Ann

Very helpful for me:
- Cuddling or a cuddle.
- Patience. Understanding.
- Being with other fellow-sufferers.
- Help when you ask for it.
- QUICK HELP when you ask professionals.
- GPs to take decisions and not wait for consultants to act. When I asked for help the last time it was a week before I saw the

consultant. All I wanted to do was start my medication again. Six months previously I had stopped taking it to see if I could cope without.

Time is a healer and in the meantime patience is needed. On the road to recovery I try to be patient with myself. I have to give myself a pat on the back for achieving the smallest of things e.g. getting up, getting dressed, washing my hair, is it OK to do a jigsaw puzzle (yes, but no more than 500 pieces). The day-unit was a real help.

My husband's patience with me is invaluable. He took over everything—cooking, cleaning, shopping, cuddling me.

Slowly, slowly over the next months I did more and more and became my useful self again.

I have made some good friends through Church. The vicars in particular have passed on some very wise words to me. I asked once 'Why is life so painful?' The response was, 'Pain is a safety valve. If it didn't exist, how would we know to save ourselves? For example, if a person put his hand into a fire, he would not know to pull his hand out if he did not feel any pain.'

Equally, how would we know the good times if we did not experience bad times?

As we go through life we learn from the experiences we have, as painful as they may be. When our first son was born we were devastated to learn that he could have been completely blind. Yet through him we have learnt so much. For example, I thought being blind meant you could see nothing at all, but in fact, most people who are registered blind have some useful vision. 6/60 vision means that someone can see at 6 metres what a 'normally sighted' person can see at 60 metres. 6/60 is the threshold which determines whether a person is officially registered blind or not. Actually, these days, people are said to be partially-sighted rather than blind. Very few people are actually completely blind. We personally know of only one little boy, who needed to have his eyes removed. Generally, if a child is born with an eye condition they have other problems too—spina bifida, cerebral palsy, deafness, to name but a few. So in fact we were very lucky that our son just has a sight difficulty.

Ann

What doesn't help is when professionals don't act as quickly as you would like them to.

When you are ill and someone says, "PULL YOURSELF TOGETHER", it is positively the last thing you want to hear. You really want to do it, but it is easier said than done when you are in the depths of despair and the only questions you are asking yourself are:

- "Why is life like this?"
- "Why is it so horrible/complicated?"
- "Why and what am I so frightened of?"
- "I cannot see my way through this and all I want is to die."

And of course, life is *not* always happy.

Chris

Friends and family definitely helped in many ways, especially when I was off the rails, psychotic and in trouble with the police. Also during my depression I received lots of encouragement and support and help with practical things like furniture, curtains, bedding. Invites out to dinners, to BBQs and to watch football also helped me gradually re-engage in things. I guess I was lucky in some ways as many of my friends around this time had either a history of mental health difficulties themselves or had relatives who had, so they were understanding. However, comments that didn't help were such as,

- "You shouldn't be hanging around with people with mental health problems," to which my response was, "What, you mean people like me?" or
- "Are you still taking pills? You don't want to be on them forever, do you?" and before I get a chance to answer someone else has spoken for me saying, "Yes, but he goes a little bit round the bend when he doesn't take them."

Being part of a mental health support group has also helped me. At one point it was the only social event I had to look forward to each week. I don't think I had ever been so isolated, and when you are that isolated you cannot see a way out of it. It served as something to get me up and about and it was a situation where you were not judged unfairly. I think going to the group slowly helped me get some confidence back. It also made me aware that there were other people in more or less the same boat, as did meeting people at the Open Door day centre, a meeting place for people with long-term mental health difficulties.

One of the main difficulties I found in recovering from my mental health difficulties was inactivity and lack of occupation. It was difficult as I had always had something to do in life. What helped me out of this situation was working within Mental Health with groups run by service users. Getting involved in a research project looking into crisis resolution, home treatment teams and the crises of others, has given me more insight into coping skills, mental health issues and recovery, and also seeing what experiences others have had.

As I couldn't receive any counselling on the NHS I contacted CRUSE bereavement. Although they didn't have an immediate appointment available I eventually began seeing a counsellor once a week for one hour. Here I could talk openly about anything going on in my life and resolve issues. Additional activities that have helped me are cycling and walking, socialising, reading—especially books related to mental health—and meditation. Keeping a journal during my stay in hospital and at home has also given me a channel to let things out, explore and reflect on the state of my health.

Hugh

Personally I need regular contact with the mental health services. The more people who have concern for me helps me considerably. I like to view it as an umbrella protecting me. When contact is lost, my mental health often suffers.

I only see my sister and family once a year at Christmas but I know I have their support in spirit.

Most of my friends are aware of my mental health problems and are sympathetic. I just need someone to be there for me. Often I just need someone to talk to. Many acquaintances are unaware of my problems and this can prove awkward.

The support group I have been involved with for five years has been a huge help. I wish my CPN (Community Psychiatric Nurse) had told me about it earlier. We meet once a week for two hours and are a self-help group, no professionals involved. We are sympathetic to each other's needs and we also arrange social activities and outings. I have made great friends with the people involved. Through this group too I have become involved in other meetings, courses and some teaching work that involves explaining my mental health history to medical students.

I find the more I do the better I am, as long as I don't attempt too much and overdo it. By keeping myself busy, I hopefully keep depression at bay. Otherwise when I start abandoning my activities and my meetings and not meeting my friends, this is the time to worry. By isolating myself I am leaving myself wide open to very bad depression. The busier I am the better I am.

I love social activities and the support group has proved invaluable in providing plenty of these.

There have been times where there have been long delays in seeing someone from the mental health services. This certainly does not help and has led to worsening of depression.

Becky

The support from my mental health community psychiatric nurse is invaluable. Having someone there, if needed, to talk things through with when times are tough or to encourage and motivate me when times are a bit better are the main sources of the support I need. Medication in the past has hindered my recovery, but now that I am taking lower doses it seems to help me sleep. However, that is the only benefit I receive. The side effects of the medication are becoming more and more distressing, even on the lower doses.

Although I now no longer see a psychologist, I was meeting with him for 2 years. This was again what I needed at this time and this period, although it was extremely challenging and hard, was a major step forward in rediscovering my life and what it has to offer.

I have also received a lot of support from a voluntary organisation, **Framework,** which gave me the practical support I needed to move into a home of my home and become more independent.

I attended a young persons' group for a number of years which helped me to develop the basic social skills and support I needed at that time. I needed the safe environment of a group and day centre to be able to develop those skills in a safe environment before I was able to move on to do more socially active things in society at large. The group was called **Stepping Stones** and it certainly was a stepping stone for me.

My friends are still few and far between but the few I now have are real friends and accept me for who I am. I now work as a cub-scout leader and have developed a friendship through this that has been my cornerstone for the last two years. The peer support group has also meant I have developed friendships and the ability to be more socially confident in a safe environment.

Voluntary work and social activities help by giving me something to look forward to and providing purpose and meaning in my life. The voluntary work especially does the latter, because it revolves around helping the service to improve and supporting other people who experience distress.

I have recently taken up yoga and although I am not spiritual, in that I do not go to church on a regular basis, I have found inner peace. The stretching and gentle exercise also helps me feel healthier in myself.

Acupuncture has also been very beneficial and has had surprisingly good results. I never thought that having needles put into your ears could help me, but it did. It helped by calming my breathing and the thoughts and hallucinations I was experiencing at the time. I have had a number of auricular acupuncture sessions since this initial session and all have had similar benefits. These benefits lasted for quite a while after the sessions as well.

What hasn't helped is the total control the Mental Health system took over me. The resulting lack of autonomy I had over my life was detrimental to my well-being and mental health.

The ongoing effects during and after admission to hospital still affects my emotions and depresses me. I do not like to think that other people will go through and have been through the same experiences as I have on those acute wards. I have been left emotionally and physically scarred by that experience. It has taken me a long time to come to terms with all the events that happened to me, and to others, on that ward, some of which you would not want to believe. I still vividly remember being pinned down and injected for daring to argue with a nurse over my treatment. I remember the lack of respect that most of the nurses had for me and the times I needed and asked to talk to a nurse, yet they would tell me 'just wait another half an hour' or 'wait till tomorrow'.

The friends I did make and the support I did get, however, were from some of the other patients. I made really good friends with one patient and he was supportive, kind and gentle. He was there for me after I had attempted suicide on the ward by slitting my wrists. He asked the nurses where I was, and if hadn't been for him I would probably now be dead. I could not, however, get the nurses to listen to me when *he* went missing and when they did find him he was dead after jumping from the car park roof. I still blame myself for not being able to get the staff to listen to me. He had been rocking in his chair for an hour before he went missing, crying out for help, but the staff just ignored him, then ignored me when he had disappeared.

Not knowing what support was available to me or what was written on my Care plan is another area that has hindered my recovery. If I had known sooner that I could get psychotherapy would I still have gone through these latter years of crisis? Would the distress have been so ingrained? If I had had a copy of my Care plan and even been involved in it from the start, I could have had a say in how I would like to be treated and my treatment would have been more effective. I must say at this point that I now have a great community nurse who involves me in all decision-making and *follows* what I need rather than *telling* me what I need. I hope that more staff can follow this approach but I know from other people who use the services that this is generally not the case.

Johanna Sharland, *Jowl Cavern,* **Encaustic Art**

Not being in control of my own life has also been made difficult by my family. Although well-meaning and out of love, they feel they must over-care and control me. It can make life more difficult when striving for independence. I struggle with saying this because I do need them and love all my family, but sometimes I feel trapped by their love and expectations. As I go through the process of finding myself I need to make mistakes for myself, but I can't do this if wrapped in cotton wool. It must be scary, for my parents especially, to let me go in this way and yes, it's scary for me at times as well, as it's safer in that cotton wool.

Society as well makes it difficult to recover. The label/diagnosis that has been stamped on me and the lack of tolerance that society has for anybody different means I am cast out of society by most people. Some people just ignore me or cross the road, while others actively discriminate. There are, however, some people in society who are more accepting and willing to find out more before judging.

The Benefits system makes it difficult to do meaningful voluntary work that is flexible with my fluctuating mental health. I cannot be on a jury, and access to work and education is limited. How can I be a part of society and feel included if society doesn't really want to include me?

Elizabeth

I gained this quote from, I think Al Anon (a support group for people living with or caring for someone with alcohol problems) when I was going through a very rough patch and it has helped me to get through, doing the things I can do and accepting what I can't.

'God give me the serenity to accept the things I cannot change, the courage to change the things I can and the wisdom to know the difference.'

I hope that it will also help others in times of difficulty.

What helps

What helps is having an understanding family and friends around you, as well as being seen quickly by professionals. What does *not* help is being on the end of a long waiting-list for access to mental health services. Regular contact is vital and the more the better, creating an umbrella effect of support.

At times I need gentle prompts to talk

Someone I can open up to, who doesn't judge

Tell me it's alright to take one step at a time

Just be yourself

I wish you would accept me for what I am like

What would you like someone to say or do?

Someone who accepts you and your illness without a fuss

Support with filling out forms eg benefits, council tax

Someone to help with practical tasks e.g. making a cup of tea, tidying the garden and not making a big deal about it

Just be there, no need to say anything

Someone to remind me Rome wasn't built in a day

I really like it when someone who I trust, listens to me

When I start to feel better, someone to motivate me to do something practical

Relapse and crisis

The important thing is that, for most of us, getting well is not necessarily permanent. When we come out of a deep depression and feel on top of the world, a relapse may be just around the corner. In the early days of depression, when everything is bewildering, you just want to get better. When you do get better you think the bad times are behind you, but then the depression strikes again.

Crisis is an absolutely appalling place to be in. Everything appears dark, there is no hope, no light at the end of the tunnel. You imagine life is never going to get any better. This is where you really do need all the help you can get so that, if you are lucky, you can resolve your crisis.

Johanna Sharland, *Pet Flames*, Watercolour

Ann

Asking for help. Husband, professionals. I know I am becoming ill if my confidence takes a nose-dive. That is:

- Cannot sort the washing out.
- Don't know what do around the house.
- Cannot find the right words.
- Not interested in food.
- Cannot sleep.
- Want to go into hospital (I want to go into hospital because I hate being alone when I am ill and the temptation of taking an overdose is too great at home).

It is hell being so low. I hate, hate, hate this illness. I am told that in many circumstances, depression is an illness of those who really care about life, people who take on too much, tire themselves out and then become ill. This is certainly the case for some of the members of Rushcliffe Support Group.

I have had to learn to say NO. So instead of instantly saying Yes, I say "I will think about it and go and check my diary."

I often think it would be wonderful to have a room somewhere where I could release my anger and frustration by smashing lots of old pots. It would also be useful to have a drop-in for mental health sufferers where they could go for a cup of tea or coffee and a chat, whether they are well or not: a place where they know they will be welcome, no matter what.

Help from professionals would be better if it wasn't so complicated to access. Even my GP was finding it very difficult to get in touch with the Crisis Team. Then when I was well, the consultant said it was my GP who could access them easily and my GP said it was the consultant. I have come to the conclusion that I have to be insistent when I am ill or not feeling myself. This is not easy. My husband fought for me this last time. I have fought for my son in the past. I have also made it known to the group that I will fight for them so long as they are sure about what they want. The Rushcliffe Support Group I belong to is great. I can go along whether I am well or ill and know that I am accepted. Sometimes, being a driver, I transport us to places. When I'm not well I know that they will not be cross, upset or too disappointed that I cannot drive, meaning that the outing has to be postponed. We find we have to postpone outings for various other reasons. This doesn't matter. We usually get there in the end. We try to accommodate all the group members' wishes. A majority rules and this seems to work.

When I became ill this last time (through trying to cope without medication), I learnt the invaluable lesson that I *cannot* cope without medication. It was a painful experience, but if I had not tried, I would never have known.

Becky

My main coping strategies when dealing with severe distress or in relapse is to take respite. The other thing I do is talk to someone I trust, currently my friend who lives with me, or my community nurse, before things get out of hand. When recovering from relapse I take every day as it comes, small step by small step. I congratulate myself for doing something small on days when it is a challenge even to do something small and challenge myself to something bigger on days when I think I can achieve it. All the time I say to myself, I have done it before, I have climbed that mountain and fallen before and climbed again, I can do it again. We all have times when we struggle and we all have different ways of coping. Learning to find those ways of coping and thinking about how to deal with those times is in itself half the battle. When I was first ill I had no coping strategies and little support. Through crisis followed by crisis and through my support group and psychologist I have learnt different ways that work for me.

At times of severe crisis I have been admitted to hospital. This is not beneficial for me as the acute ward is not a therapeutic place to be and I have no doubt whatsoever that it is detrimental to my mental health.

If I had a magic wand I would want somewhere I could go that is peaceful, pleasant, quiet and therapeutic. There would be people there I could trust, to talk to and receive support, not just by medication but through other complementary therapies and peer support groups. I would want a tailored approach to my support where I had a full say in what would be useful. I would want to be able to access this support *before* I had a crisis, not when I was in a crisis i.e. when I recognised the signs of relapse, as this would make my recovery time quicker and more successful.

Hugh

Once again, getting up in the morning is what I need to do. Over recent years, however bad I have been feeling I have always managed to force myself to get up. Secondly, just to let it wash over me, not to worry too much and to try and let the depression run its course.

Elizabeth

I don't want to talk about my past as it is too hard and it has become blurred for me. I have moved on and have a future now. It's like I have woken up and come into the light. I have something to live for. I have purpose in my life. Life was dark and everything was grey, now everything is colour and light. These last six months alone have moved me away from my past towards this new life. I am full of hope and love again, eager to experience the new and exciting experiences on offer. Going out and meeting new people and seeing new places might not seem exciting to you, but for someone who never dared to experience everyday joys, it is new and wonderful for me.

To anyone going through a rough patch in their life, and I have been through many, I would tell them there is light at the end of tunnel, no matter how bleak it may seem at the moment. I and many others have proved that a glimmer of light is a beacon of hope and that hope can turn into joy and love for life again. You are not alone!

There are many sorts of crisis

We have all been through the process of getting ill, getting well and then relapsing. Crisis comes in different forms. For some it is a very certain apocalyptic moment and for others it is a very slow descent to what seems like hell.

We all hate being low, and no matter how often it has happened to us, we feel we will never get out of it.

Some of us, when recovering from a crisis, take very small steps towards recovery. For others a manic phase may take over and everything becomes extremely hyperactive.

Dean Kemp, *Life Rider,* Pencil

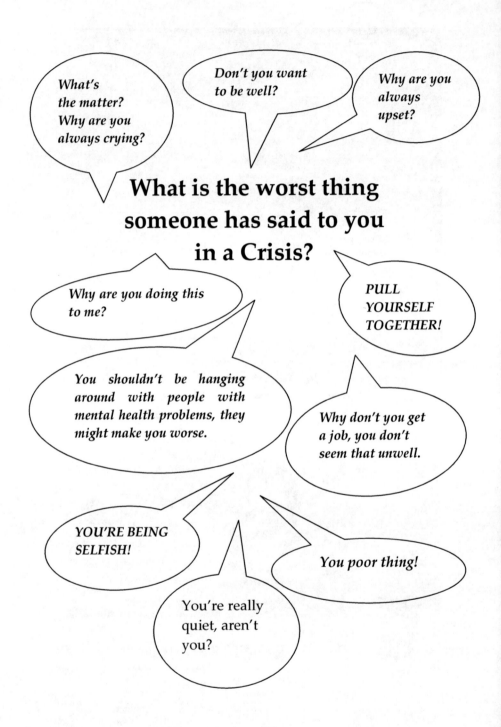

Corinne Smith, *Grey Patch*, Charcoal

Support

We have already mentioned support by the Mental Health services and by peer support. The other obvious element is family and friends. Families can be really important. If members of your family are sympathetic they can be invaluable. Unfortunately many family members will have no prior knowledge or experience of mental health problems so can be of little help.

Friends too can be of great importance. However, you sometimes have to gauge which friends to tell, ones you know will be sympathetic, and which friends not to tell because they may spread gossip.

Becky

Practical support is sometimes more important than emotional support, and just talking is important. When I was moving into my new place and living on my own for the first time, talking about how I would cope was important, but not as important as being helped with the stress of the actual move. I had no furniture, no money and none of the essentials. I had never had a home of my own. I didn't know how to pay bills or how to read the meter. The simple things people take for granted I needed someone to help me with. I couldn't catch a bus or go to the local shop on my own. I needed to work on this and, no matter how much talking and listening and advising can help, *practical* support is essential in overcoming these hurdles if the move to be a success. Fortunately I had support from a voluntary organisation and my family and friends.

Other essential forms of support from friends and family are; acceptance that I am the way I am and supporting my decisions; letting me be independent and letting me make my own mistakes, but being there when I need them to be there; having someone to listen unconditionally and be caring and supportive of what I need help with at the time; taking the time to try and understand some of the issues. I don't expect everyone to understand completely—caring enough to want to understand and supporting my decisions, is all I need.

My peer support group has been invaluable. I have also gained peer support in other ways as well as through the support group. When I was admitted to hospital the other patients were my allies and sometimes the only people who could help. I have attended a day centre and a young people's group, both of which have helped me to talk to other people who are experiencing similar difficulties with life. Through interacting with my peers I have been able to discover new coping strategies, and feel safe in trying them out. I am able to be myself, and if I am feeling down, or experiencing hallucinations, the other people accept me for who I am and what I am like at that time.

Society accepts only those who fit into what society sees as being 'normal', but there is no such thing as 'normal' and anyway I do not fit in with the stereotypical image of what is expected. What would help me most is if society could accept that everyone is unique, that differences in the human race are valuable to society. I might not be able to hold down a job but I give in other ways. This may be unpaid voluntary work, but nonetheless it contributes to society. I don't want people to look down on me because I claim benefits. Neither do I want to be forced into paid employment that will make my health worse just because it looks good. I don't want to be treated as a second-class citizen just because I have mental health difficulties. I want people to accept that when I am ill I am more of a danger to myself than others, that I need support and a caring hand to hold me as I struggle through, instead of enforced treatment that is unsuitable and can sometimes be dangerous. I want my voice to be heard as much as anyone else's instead of being trampled down and hidden away from view. Society pretends we don't exist and that there is some kind of magic cure, but we do exist and there is no magic cure or pill.

Going into a different room

Having someone in your life who speaks up for you

Jigsaw puzzles

Having people I trust around me, people who don't judge me

Helping others helps me

Space outside the mental health services, to talk and reflect and know it won't go any further

What helps you, practically and emotionally?

Being needed, even if it's only by the dog!

Having a purpose in my life, a meaning for my existence

A supportive partner and someone who can help with all the practical stuff

Financial support – enough money to live on without having to worry about finances

Reading, to take my mind somewhere else

Playing the drums or the guitar or listening to music

Meetings, especially a support group and somewhere I can feel safe to talk in a group and be myself

Support is so important

As mentioned, the peer support group is really really helpful. Friends and family can also be very important, and although they will not fully understand unless they have previously had experience of mental health problems, they can still at least be sympathetic and care about your state of mind. Practical support from friends and family is also vital, and help with those everyday jobs that need doing, such as hoovering and gardening, as at times even opening the mail can seem a huge task.

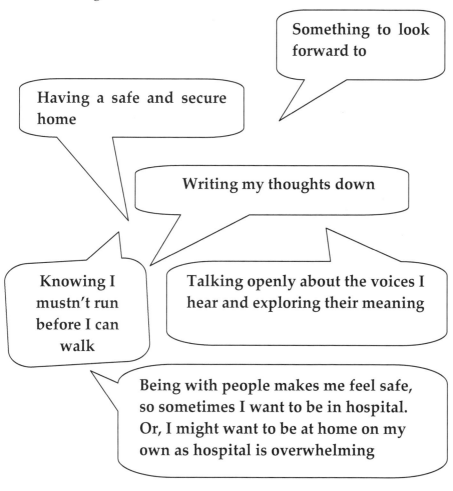

Something to look forward to

Having a safe and secure home

Writing my thoughts down

Knowing I mustn't run before I can walk

Talking openly about the voices I hear and exploring their meaning

Being with people makes me feel safe, so sometimes I want to be in hospital. Or, I might want to be at home on my own as hospital is overwhelming

Discrimination

We have all suffered from this; children at school avoiding you because you are different; at work, being ostracised; not getting a job you were more than qualified for.

The general public are still largely ignorant about mental health problems. They listen to the bigots and go along with them. The tabloids are largely responsible for spreading a great deal of rubbish about mental health. The stigma this causes can greatly affect sufferers with these problems.

1 in 4
by Ann

Ann

For myself, I find it very difficult to admit that I have a mental illness.

Why?

Maybe I see it as a weakness. Maybe I am ashamed that I have taken overdoses in the past. Maybe it is because I cannot prevent another bout of depression. I don't know why I have these feelings. Maybe we all expect too much of one another. I have had to learn that nothing is perfect. I have had to lower my standards. I have learnt to compare my results with those of others. In the process, I have realised that I have done the job better in many cases.

When my son became depressed at the age of ten, people who should have known better were telling me that children 'can't become depressed'. I worried about this until he broke his arm and we attended Children's Outpatients. There in the corner of the waiting area was a display on children and depression. My son eventually attended children's and adolescents' psychiatric hospital but he didn't want to go during school hours because he didn't want to have to explain his absence.

I thought something was wrong with my son when he wasn't following his usual sleep pattern, was crying at the drop of a hat and wanted me to push him down the stairs. When he grabbed hold of a kitchen knife and was running it lightly across his wrists we did eventually get help for him. At one stage he spent a few weeks in hospital. Various medications were tried and eventually Venlafaxine was settled upon.

His main problem was that he lacked confidence; if he wasn't the best at something then he was a failure in his own eyes. He has had therapy along the way and with good results at A-Level (1xA and 2xBs), he is now at a top university and coming 20th in his year.

University has been very understanding of his health, allowing him to repeat a year and giving him extensions on handing in pieces of work.

We do not think that we ever put pressure on either of our sons, but we may have done without realising.

I was talking to one of Christopher's teachers about his mental health. When I said I suffered too, she said, 'No!?' There seems to be this assumption that people who are mentally ill should have a certain look about them. My husband made a remark about the school caretaker who killed the two young girls in 2002. 'He doesn't look mad.'

Can anyone tell, for example, whether a person is a murderer, a thief, or a liar? If this were the case, the police would have their crimes solved in no time.

I have not personally experienced discrimination, but friends have. One wanted to take out holiday insurance but when she mentioned her mental health the rate went sky-high. She didn't tell anyone after that experience.

Another friend couldn't decide whether to reveal her illness when she applied for teacher training college. She was frightened that they would reject her application. Her psychiatrist advised her that if she really wanted to do the course, but felt her mental health would be counted against her, that she should just not mention it. She went ahead, trained as a teacher and served for many years very successfully.

Becky

I hate being on benefits. I'd rather be well and able to work just like the majority of people in society, but I can't. It has taken me a long time to accept that at the moment I can't do paid work and won't be able to for quite a while, if ever, and I hate it. I hate it because of how other people view it. The drive from the government to get all disabled people back to work is a scary prospect for me as every time I have done paid work I have become acutely unwell again and ended up back in hospital. Do I have to go through this again to prove to them I can't work and that their policy is making me ill just thinking about the pressure? There are also the adverts about benefit fraud that are shown on television, the 'NO IFS, NO BUTS!' 'Benefit fraud is a crime'. This just heightens the anxiety about claiming benefits in the first place. It took me a long time before I did claim anything because of the stigma surrounding being on benefits. There are lots of people who don't claim any benefits or who don't ask for support because of the stigma. There are no adverts on television that help people to know that they can claim, that having a mental health difficulty is not a sign or something to be afraid of, and that help is available.

Discrimination because of the mental health system and because of being in the system has had a major impact upon me and my ability to move forward. Just being labelled with a diagnosis puts me in a box. This box then surrounds me for life and is something I find hard to escape from.

Hugh

When I first began to receive benefits many years ago I felt a lot of stigma. But as the years have gone on, and as I realise that my illness makes it almost impossible to work full-time, I have got used to the situation and now do not feel uncomfortable at all.

As I mentioned earlier, there is still a great stigma attached to mental health. Personally, I take great care who I tell and who I do not tell about my personal history. It only takes one person with the wrong attitude to spread malicious gossip, for your world to start crumbling.

Apart from my sister, brother-in-law, niece and nephew who I only see once a year at Christmas, the remaining members of my family are cousins who tend to congregate only at funerals. Some of these cousins are more aware than others about my mental wellbeing, but on the whole I would say they are pretty supportive.

There has certainly been an improvement in the attitude of the media over recent years. I am thinking in particular about the excellent Stephen Fry programmes about manic depression. Yet there are still very unhelpful and outdated attitudes in the tabloids.

Clearly stigma and discrimination are very unhelpful and can impede one's progress to better health.

I have combated this discrimination largely by being careful who I tell about my mental health history. Other ways to combat discrimination are by working with groups, doing courses and going to meetings to foster a better understanding of mental health.

Society needs to become more understanding and responsive to mental health sufferers if the stigma attached to it is to diminish and, in the ideal world, die away completely.

Anon

Receiving benefits is demoralising. I would much rather be able to work and feel normal and that I am contributing rather than being a burden on society. If I'm out and about and somebody asks me what I do, I make something up.

I never tell anybody that I have mental health problems. The only people who know about my difficulties are people who have had them themselves. Mention schizophrenia to anybody and I think they immediately think of the murders you hear about on the television. It gets bad press.

It means I spend a lot of time dodging people in my neighbourhood, hoping that they won't ask me what I do as I've no answer. I never tell anybody about my problems unless they are mental health professionals or unless they have had similar experiences, and even then I am still reluctant.

Media and Stigma

Television is starting to change its attitude towards people with mental health difficulties, as Ann explains, but the newspapers still have a long way to go.

Ann

Some really good programmes featuring mental health are now being shown on television. Long may they continue. I feel sure these programmes help educate and inform the general public, especially when someone like Stephen Fry shares his experiences. It is frustrating when people do not understand, but then there are some things in life that I will never understand, therefore how can we expect everyone to be familiar with our difficulties?

Perceptions of mental illness

Mental illness is seen as a weakness, both in the sufferer and in society as a whole. Pressure from the media always seems to stereotype mental health problems as being dangerous to others and that people with these problems should be avoided. How much easier to have a broken leg! Society certainly needs to be more understanding and aware. Challenging stigma through television programmes and the written word will certainly help.

Johanna Sharland, *Dandelion Clock*, Watercolour

Recovery

Life today

As stated earlier, for every down there is an up. Life does get better as we learn to live with our illness. The coping strategies we put into place reinforce and strengthen and make it less likely we will plummet to the depths of despair again.

It would be wonderful to think that recovery could be really complete but the reality is that most of us have to learn to live with our illness.

Becky

I live with my voices and the ups and downs as a part of my life. Living with these experiences and managing them in the best way I can, for me is important. I may never be free from these experiences but I can still live a full and meaningful life. The process of recognising this has, for me, been the recovery, or rediscovery, that I needed. I now live for me, and every day I say to myself that if I want to do something, 'Why not?' It might take me longer or I might need to do it in a different way but I can still do it. Just like someone in a wheelchair who can adapt and not be ruled by the boundaries their disability could impose, I too have adapted and am not bound by the limitations of my illness.

I used to be bound by the effects of experiencing recurrent distress, and every day the unusual experiences and the treatment I received for a long time told me I was ill, that I would be ill for life and that I could not recover. Realising that this isn't true, that I can have a meaningful and fulfilling life, that I may not always be a mental health service user, and by finding myself and following my dreams, I can now live life for myself instead of being on that treadmill.

I am me, with all my faults, and society can either accept that or not, but I am not going to change simply because society does not tolerate difference, and nor should you. Recovery has been about finding myself and rediscovering what is important to *me*, not what is important to others.

Ann

I have accepted that I need medication and that the medication does not stop me from having low periods, but that these are not as bad, or as long, as without medication. Also, psychotherapy has helped me think about life in a different way. Rushcliffe Mental Health Support Group helps me as there I find people who understand me, and with whom I feel comfortable. It also provides me with a social life as we go out on day trips and to the cinema and theatre.

Chris

In comparison with how I was one year ago things have changed a great deal. One year ago my life was rock bottom. I was freshly diagnosed with bipolar with no insight into my illness or the world of psychiatry. I was discharged from hospital, manic and taking a high dose of antipsychotics. I was homeless (but staying in a B&B), penniless, in debt with fines outstanding and with the threat of arrest for non-payment of these fines. I had no partner, no friends and no occupation.

One year on and my life is more back on track. Firstly I have a much better understanding of mental health issues and my own condition and know that there is a lot of support out there. I am still on medication, but a medication and dosage of my choosing. I have my own flat, and although I'm not rich, my finances are more in order. I have less debt and fines are being paid off. I have a very understanding and lovely girlfriend, many more good friends and a fairly good social life. I could not have imagined any of this becoming a reality one year ago as I stared out from the mists of depression and confusion.

How I would define recovery?

Recovery is a gradual process with many aspects of yourself slowly coming back to life. For me the key to recovering is to have hope of improvement or at least hope of hope. Take time out to heal and allow yourself to take small steps forward. Don't try to do too much too soon. A big part of recovery is about acceptance; accepting that you have a mental health condition but realizing at the same time that you are not alone and that a large proportion of people have mental health issues. Gaining insight into your condition will aid the healing process, and reflection and comparison of how you have been in the past, compared to how you are now, can make you realise that you are on the path to recovery. In the final stages I would say that self-belief and confidence as well as inner strength begin to come back to you and you can begin to take responsibility for your own situation.

I shall write down a few words that a friend wrote on recovery;

Recovery is not the same as cure,
Recovery is about growth,
Recovery is about taking back control over one's life,
Everyone's recovery journey is different and deeply personal.

Use this for some confidence and empowerment:

I have the right to change my mind,
I have the right simply to be myself, without having to act for others' benefit,
I have the right to set my own priorities,
I have the right to make reasonable requests of others,
I have the right to be listened to and taken seriously,
I have the right to be illogical in making decisions.

Recovering Life

Some people who experience a psychotic episode only ever have one episode. Some people have never accessed the Mental Health services even though they experience psychosis, because they have naturally learnt how to cope.

All of us writing this book know that we will probably suffer with mental health problems for life and the key is how we will, and do, deal with them. We have our ups and downs and we have to accept that our life will be like that. This acceptance is part of our recovery. There is no miracle cure. It is may help to know that it is usually the more intelligent people that suffer in this way.

Recovery *is* possible. You would expect a person in a wheelchair, who is not expected to ever walk again, to have a full and meaningful life. The same is true for somebody who has mental health problems. You can still live a full and meaningful life, even with mental health difficulties. The process of recovery is learning how to cope with these difficulties, to live with them and, despite them, to maximise the potential that you have.

What does it feel like to come through from the darkest moment?

Awakened

Bright

Vivid noises I can hear the bees and birds

Everything was grey now colourful even
when it is raining

Lively

Regained trust in people

Over-stimulating

Thoughts changed the cup is half full

Beautiful

Feel like dancing and laughing

All so clear I have been in a hole and now
I have come out

Very perceptive and extremely aware

Meaning to life and I have something to
get up for

'flying home'
Although recovery can seem like an
endless journey, remind your self
that you are going in the right
direction, and one day you will
get to your destination.

Chris Heap, *Flying Home*

Top Tips

As we go through life, suffering from mental health problems, we all pick up useful information that may help us in our journey. Finding a support group is, in my experience, an essential tool. Keeping busy and always having something to look forward to is vital. Talking as much as possible to peers, family and friends helps get the problems out in the open. Another tip is to write down as much as possible. Things you have done, however insignificant, and things you plan to do. This can be very therapeutic and can help keep life in perspective.

Becky

You only get one life. Live it. Discover what you want to get out of it and say to yourself 'Why not!' Then do it for you.

Life has its ups and downs, its thrills and spills, but it's just a ride. Enjoy it and remember that you can get through the downs no matter how dark they seem at the time. I have been there and probably will be again and my way up is just taking each day and each task one at a time. If on a bad day I can get up and make a cup of tea that's great. The old sayings are the best: 'Don't run before you can walk'. But do praise yourself each step of that walk.

Don't blame yourself. We can all look back in hindsight. We all make mistakes. We are, after all, human, but we can learn from those mistakes and move forward. I spent my life looking at what I couldn't do instead of looking at what I could, and when I turned it round I then discovered I could do more than I ever thought I could.

Take control over your life—you only get one. Get support in doing this as you will find it invaluable to have like minds together.

Talk to and be with your peers. They may or may not have experienced similar distress themselves but having people around you who understand and can empathise, who are honest and trustworthy, are essential in life.

Anon

I would say listen to the doctors. Although they are not magicians they may know a little thing or two!

Hugh

Talk. Listen. Keep busy. Try to stay positive. Remember to take your medication.

Ann

1. Take your medicine.
2. Remember that no one and nothing is perfect.
3. Do things your way if it works for you.
4. Reason things out whenever you can. It's good to ask lots of questions of lots of people and then come to your own conclusion.
5. Be kind to yourself. That is, don't judge yourself any more than you would judge anyone else.
6. Set realistic targets and then treat yourself on attaining them (my treats are a bar of chocolate, an outing or watching a DVD).

Hugh

Getting involved helps the process of mental recovery. Thanks to being an active member of my support group I have become involved with further mental health activities. Once a month we have a 'core group' meeting where service users (me and Becky), carers, social workers, occupational therapists, community care workers etc get together to discuss what has gone on in the previous month and to plan for the next month in the Rushcliffe area.

I have become involved with a local service user organisation which works to help those suffering with mental ill-health. Through this organisation I have been on training courses. This has led to me being involved in teaching mental health students (and general medical students) through my own history of mental illness.

Another course has led on to us conducting interviews of people who have used the CRHT (Crisis Resolution and Home Treatment) teams, to find out about their experiences and their views.

Becky

There has been a drive in recent years to involve people who use the mental health services in decision-making and in delivering care.

Areas of involvement in all aspects of the Nottinghamshire Mental Health Trust are increasing, including delivery of training, research, trust policy and care delivery itself. I am involved in some of these myself, and although I have to do it voluntarily because of being on benefits, I have gained considerably by the increase in my self-esteem and feelings of self-worth. It has given meaning to my life and I now fight to make a difference for others.

Our Top Tips for recovering life

- Try to keep optimistic (not always easy)

- Don't blame yourself

- Try to take control of your life

- Arrange your life to best suit your own needs

- Take time for yourself and be kind to yourself

- Don't forget, Rome wasn't built in a day—it was built brick by brick, so take those first small steps, one at a time

- Get involved

Getting involved

Thanks to the Rushcliffe Mental Health Support Group some of us have become involved in other groups and courses, in teaching and in research on a voluntary basis. This has proved extremely informative and cathartic. It seems that the more that you do, the more avenues open up. The optimum situation is doing enough to fulfil you without overdoing it and wearing yourself out.

Social activities

Apart from providing support for all its members, the group offers a wide range of social activities. We often go to the cinema and theatre and sometimes tenpin bowling. One of our member's family has a holiday home in Cornwall and provision is made for us to visit at least once a year. Personally I've been lucky enough to go and in fact I have been down there seven times. It is always a welcome respite from the hectic modern life.

We have excursions to local places of interest, sometimes going as far afield as Derbyshire. A few years ago group members were lucky enough to have a holiday in Strathpeffer in the Highlands of Scotland. This was thoroughly enjoyed by all.

Last year, with funding, we arranged a holiday to Turkey. Unfortunately, due to various circumstances, this was not a great success, but the group members did manage to bond even more than usual.

We continue to arrange a very busy schedule of social activities and we plan another visit to Cornwall in September. If we can gain more funding, even another foreign holiday is not out of the question.

John Sharland, *Reliable Robin*, Watercolour

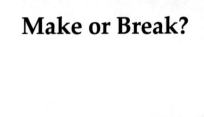

Make or Break?

We all have different experiences of mental health problems: manic-depression (sometimes called bi-polar disorder); hearing voices; schizophrenia; paranoia; psychosis and many more. What we all share is an alienation from society. We all have to find our way through life, facing many pitfalls along the way. Appropriate help and advice is vitally important and we have to put ourselves in the hands of the professionals. Of equal importance, maybe even of greater importance, is to find a group of peers, also suffering from mental health problems, whom we can rely on so that together we can face whatever life throws up.

Alex

I first sought help for my depression from my GP when I was 18. He prescribed antidepressants. Since then I have taken so many different types that I can't remember most of their names. My GP also referred me to a psychiatrist at the West Middlesex Hospital in London, where I was living. At first, I was afraid of being labelled 'mentally disturbed' so I didn't tell anyone I was receiving psychiatric treatment, or that I was taking medications for depression. It was the beginning of a hidden side to my life that would endure for many years. Stigma has been an uncomfortable adjunct throughout my years of wrestling with mental illness.

As I grew older, my condition became worse. As well as taking various medications, I tried three programmes of counselling. They all helped to some degree, but nothing worked permanently. In the end, I just couldn't go on and suffered a complete mental breakdown. This was a nightmarish experience from which I'm still recovering. It plunged me into new depths of despair and terror that I hadn't experienced before. I felt I had lost everything and would never recover.

By this time, my condition couldn't be concealed. However, family and friends were highly supportive. This was crucially important to my recovery. Looking back, I see the experience of breakdown as an important turning point, though I definitely don't want to repeat it. Perhaps I had struggled too hard, for too long, with too little support. In any event, new opportunities opened up through the health services.

I have nothing but gratitude and appreciation for the health professionals who have given me so much time and attention over the years. Mental health is not the easiest or best funded area of medicine and there is no great public clamour for more resources to be devoted to it. Perhaps this is because mental illness is often invisible. It's also little understood by the public, even though it is quite common. However, recently there have been some very good efforts at raising public awareness through the media.

Family and friends have sometimes found it hard to understand my condition. One of their questions is: 'what caused it?' The problem with this question is that there is no agreement about the answer. Sometimes mental illness is attributed to previous life experience or trauma and I'm sure this can be the case. But it doesn't fit all instances. Sometimes it's difficult to distinguish possible causes from compounding symptoms such as addiction, exhaustion, inability to cope with stress, eating disorders, 'chemical imbalance' etc.

In my own case, there are clear pointers towards life events: unhappy childhood; sexual abuse; early parental loss. But I remain skeptical about simplistic answers to the 'why?' question. All my experience leads me to believe that mental illness is both complex and intractable. So I'm more concerned to direct my energies towards active recovery in the present.

I find creativity to be therapeutic. I attend a local day centre where, among other things, I have found a renewed interest in art and have developed my skills in a satisfying way. Physical exercise is important for me as well. I may not feel like doing it but I certainly feel better if I make the effort. Relationships are important. As well as family and friends, I try to get out and meet as wide a variety of people as possible. I try to laugh, dance and sing, whenever I can.

I believe it's important to take responsibility for my own recovery. I'm grateful for all the support that's available to me and I've made good use of it. But the only person who can really steer my personal journey, who can manage my recovery from this mysterious condition—is *me*.

Hugh

In conclusion, I would say that my mental health problems really have ruined my life. My early academic aspirations were dashed and I had to settle for second best.

My GP had very little understanding of the problem and prescribed me phenobarbitone (which amazed a doctor recently). My frequent lows ruined my school career and also my teaching career as I tended to start and never finish things.

My illness wore my parents out and I blame myself for my mother's early death. I couldn't support my father properly after his stroke because of my illness and he died soon afterwards as well.

Mental health problems destroyed my marriage and my relationship with my fiancée. I have made many friends over the years but I have lost most of them because I tend to cut people off when illness strikes.

Becky

Life throws at us numerous challenges that will make us or break us. I see life as a process of discovering who we are. I, like many, have come through this process and out the other end. I have come through the endless dark out into the light, but I know my journey is never ending. I used to ask 'Why *me*?' The answer would be a deathly silence, but I know now that life's ups and downs have been making me who I am.

Now, through my experiences, I want to help others come through as well. Just by telling my story I can give hope. The more I give, the more I receive. Life is short and I have learnt to say, 'Why Not!'

Everyone's journey is different and unique to them but that's what makes us great. Accepting who you are right now can be hard, but worthwhile. We are all wonderful, loveable and valuable human beings just as we are. I wanted to be thin like the models in the magazines. I wanted what I could not have. I did not realise for such a long time that I was unhappy not with my size, my external me, but with my essential core, my inner me. I have now turned that corner and you can too.

Recover your dreams

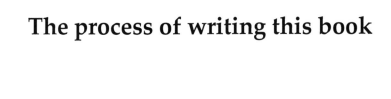

The process of writing this book

It can be hard writing down your thoughts and feelings. It's like reliving the past and opening yourself up for others to see. We have all, in writing this book, come one step further to discovering who we are and how far we have come. It has been cathartic and inspiring. We have shared turmoil and pain, love and laughter in the process.

We have become closer to each other, delved into our hearts, and we hope that in the process you, the reader, have learnt about the ongoing process of discovering recovery from mental health distress.

Elizabeth

It has been a bit upsetting at times to do this, but to write is very cathartic. By getting things off my chest I feel unburdened. It's also wonderful to know that, hopefully, it will help others when they read my story.

Acknowledgments

Thanks must go to—

Christopher (pseudonym) for his patience in scanning/preparing these drawings ready for the book.

Other line drawings have been done by Ann (pseudonym)

Bubbles/spider diagrams were created as a group activity.

The Lost Artists Club:
for all your wonderful art work

To Graham, Sue and Charles at **Writersworld** we want to say a special thank-you to you for all for your help and support in producing our book, and the honest, practical advice that has turned our dreams into reality. It has been lovely working with you all and we would recommend you to anyone thinking of writing their own book.

To Ann and all at the **Friary Drop-In Centre**, we want to thank you for your help when we first formed the support group, as without this support we could not have got started all those years ago. Currently you still provide support for some of our group members and many people with mental health difficulties in this area. Keep up the good work.

To Shirley Jeffs and all at the **Open Door Day Centre**—without your support, Shirley, and the valuable support many of our members continue to receive from Open Door, the group would not have been formed.

Framework's Rushcliffe House-hold Service
Framework works with, and values, people who are experiencing poor mental health, in order to maximise their potential for living in their own home in the community. This is based on the belief that everyone has a right to social inclusion.

Rushcliffe Mental Health Outreach Team
This team is made up of psychiatrists, social workers, occupational therapists and mental health nurses. They work in the community from a local base, with people who have mental health difficulties.

Voluntary Sector Liaison Service
We receive funding each year, called Grant Aid, through the Voluntary Sector Liaison Service (Adult Social Care and Health). We are very grateful for their ongoing support without which we would not be able to run the group.

Awards for All
We have been partly funded by Awards for All this year.

Self Help Nottingham
The main organisers of the Rushcliffe Support group, and many similar groups, have been supported by Self Help Nottingham, for which we are very grateful. Without their invaluable support we would not have flourished.

Rushcliffe Mental Help Support Group

We are a small self help group offering support, information, activities and regular weekly meetings. We have all experienced mental health difficulties. Through the trust we are also involved in various activities, from training, to attending meetings, to helping service users have a say in service developments. We have been running the group for over fifteen years now and always welcome new people at any time.

👍 The group is open to all affected by mental health difficulties

👍 It is important to note that individuals can come as little or as often as they like.

👍 It is a fun, supportive and friendly group

👍 Individuals can self refer

Rushcliffe Mental Health Support Group

For further information and for self refer, ring Self Help Nottingham
Information line
0115 911 1661 (Monday to Friday 9am till 1.00pm). Your details
will be passed on to us and we will then contact you.
OR you can contact us by post at 4 Holme Road, Bingham,
Notts, NG13 8DZ
OR by email bshawmh@inbox.com

Weekly meetings	Support Friendship Reassurance Understanding
Social outings Days out Theatre Cinema Country parks Holidays and short breaks	**Information** Medication Other services and areas of support Informal ideas
Helping Improve services In hospital In the community	**Training and research**
Open and accessible All welcome including carers	

The Lost Artists Club

The Art Unites Us!

We are a diverse collection of creative types who share work, news and ideas. We swap skills and experiment with various artistic mediums. We exhibit, perform live, produce publications and CDs.

Some of us keep in touch online in the Creative Café.

Membership (18+) is free and entitles you to a copy of **BLANK SPACE**, our regular newsletter, which has reviews and artistic features as well as LAC news, members' art, writings, a profile section and a regular comic strip. It also informs us about free & inexpensive events locally.

We have a stock of equipment - cameras, recording devices & suchlike which are available for loan to members for a small deposit.

We have a themed taster session at every Creative Gathering.

These Creative Gatherings are held on the **Second Saturday** of each month **2-5pm**.

We always welcome more people, so *do come & join us* at—

City Arts (Nottingham) Ltd,
NRSB,
Ortzen Street off Peveril Street,
Radford, Nottingham,
NG7 4BN.

Tel: 0115 978 2463

Email: lostartistsclub@yahoo.co.uk

Online Group: http://creativecafe.ning.com/

Glossary

Advocate

A person who speaks on behalf of another.

Carer

A person who supports someone else. Could be a family member or friend.

Community mental health nurse (CMHN)

A CMHN can also be known as a CPN (Community Psychiatric Nurse). They work as part of a community mental health team, often based at GPs' surgeries. They can have specialist areas of experience such as children, elderly people, drug or alcohol problems.

Community Mental Health Team (CMHT)

CMHTs are found in each local area where they support people with longer-term mental health difficulties within the community. Support is offered by psychiatrists, nurses, occupational therapists, social workers and other mental health workers.

Counsellor

Counselling is described as a 'talking' treatment. It can help people to manage a wide range of problems.

Access to counselling services can be difficult to arrange in the NHS.

General practitioner (GP)

The doctor can be the first point of contact for many patients. They can work singly or as part of a multi-agency team providing mental health care.

Health visitor

They offer advice on general health, with special training in child health.

Healthcare Commission

This body assesses the effectiveness of services delivered by the NHS. As part of its role it carries out surveys of mental health services including evaluation of patient feedback.

Occupational Therapist

They work within the community, day hospitals and secure psychiatric units.

Their work is based on helping individuals become more confident and build the skills needed to live in the community. They also focus on anxiety management and assertiveness training.

Patient Advice and Liaison Services (PALS)

Some of their functions were previously run by community health councils.

PALS are established in each NHS Trust and work to help patients sort out treatment problems within that Trust.

Any problem they can't solve within the Trust will be referred probably to:

Psychiatrist

Psychiatrists are medically trained doctors who have specialised in mental health.

They can work in hospitals, the community as part of multi-agency teams, or individual secure units.

Psychologist

Unlike psychiatrists, psychologists do not have to be medically trained. They must have a degree in psychology plus work experience. They can further qualify by studying a particular branch of psychology such as clinical psychology, counselling psychology etc.

Psychotherapist

A psychotherapist may be a psychiatrist, a psychologist or other mental health professional with special training.

Psychotherapy works to find out why you feel as you do and why you respond to others the way you do.

Service User

A service user is someone who uses the NHS (National Health Service) services and within this book refers to people who use the mental health services of the NHS. The majority of people who use services dislike the term 'service user' and alternatives have been sought, e.g. in America they are also known as consumers, patients, sufferers and service recipients. However, the problem is not the wording of the definition but its *meaning*. Once again it is a label and for this reason no one definition will ever be preferable to the rest. People who experience distress want above all things to be known for themselves—an individual who at times experiences mental health distress. In this book the individual contributor's preference means that different terms have been used to refer to those experiencing distress.

Social worker

Social workers offer support for a variety of social rather than medical needs, and not only within mental health.

Approved Social Worker

Approved social workers (ASW) have been trained in specific functions under the Mental Health Act (1983).

Survivor

A survivor is a term used by those who have used the mental health services, and have survived using them. Again, it is a matter of personal preference as to what term someone will use, if anything at all.

Resources

National Mind

Mind is the leading mental health charity in England and Wales.

Mind Info Line:

Monday to Friday, 9am till 5pm

Telephone: 0845 766 0163

Website: www.mind.org.uk

15-19 Broadway, London E15 4BQ

There are around 200 local Mind associations (LMAs) in England and Wales. Your local Mind association can be found either by ringing the Mind information line or by looking on the Mind website.

Rethink

Rethink is the largest national voluntary sector provider of mental health services, with 340 services and more than 130 support groups. It helps over 48,000 people every year through its services, support groups, and by providing information on mental health problems.

Website: www.rethink.org

Email for general enquiries: info@rethink.org

General enquiries: 0845 456 0455

Sane

Sane undertakes research and raises awareness and respect for people with mental illness, and their families, and helps to secure better services.

Website: www.sane.org.uk

Saneline provides help and information to those experiencing mental health problems, and to their families and carers, through SANEline and SANEmail.

Email: sanemail@sane.org.uk

SANEline is a national out-of-hours telephone helpline offering emotional support and information for people affected by mental health problems.

Telephone: 0845 767 8000 6pm till 11pm everyday

Samaritans

Samaritans provides confidential, non-judgmental emotional support, 24 hours a day, for people experiencing feelings of distress or despair, including those which could lead to suicide.

Website: www.samaritans.org

Email: jo@samaritans.org

Telephone: 08457 90 90 90

P.O. Box 9090, Stirling, FK8 2SA

MDF, The BiPolar Organisation
(Manic Depression Fellowship)

MDF The BiPolar Organisation works to enable people affected by bipolar disorder/manic depression, to take control of their lives. MDF currently provides the following:

- Self-help groups
- Information and publications

146

- Employment advice
- Self-management training programme
- 24-hour legal advice line for employment; legal issues; benefits and debt issues
- Travel insurance scheme.

Website: www.mdf.org.uk

Telephone: 08456 340540

Castle Works, 21 St. George's Road, London, SE1 6ES

Hearing Voices Network

Hearing Voices Network offers information, support and understanding to people who hear voices and those who support them.

www.hearing-voices.org

Email: info@hearing-voices.org

HVN, 79 Lever St. Manchester, M1 1FL

The Friary Drop-In Centre

The *Friary Drop-In* was founded by Ann Bremner MBE with the help of a few volunteers, 20 years ago. It started out as a one-morning-a-week coffee and biscuits drop-in for the homeless, those living in temporary accommodation and the poorer unemployed in the locality.

The Drop-In Centre is now open 5 days a week from 9.00 am to 5.30 pm for the staff to provide advice and guidance on welfare benefits, housing, health and community care.

Website: www.friarydrop-in.org.uk

46 Musters Road, West Bridgford, Nottingham NG2 7PR, UK

Self Help Nottingham

Self Help Nottingham is a charity that provides support and development opportunities for self-help groups and their members in Greater Nottingham. They have an information line and produce an annual directory of support groups in the area.

Ormiston House, 32-36 Pelham Street, Nottingham NG1 2EG

www.selfhelp.org.uk

telephone: 0115 9111655 (Monday-Friday, 9,00am -1.00pm

Illustrations

'Wonderfully Strange'

by
Becky Shaw

- ➢ If you've ever been 'labelled'
- ➢ If you've ever worried about using mental health services
- ➢ If you've ever wondered how you'd cope if someone you know has mental health problems—

—then read 'Wonderfully Strange'. It is an account of Becky's journey through the mental health system, plus practical help on how to manage, where to go and how to survive.

As someone labelled psychotic, bulimic and a depressive, she knows at first hand how it feels to be adrift in a system which she didn't understand and which didn't address her needs.

Alongside the story of her survival she also offers help and advice to others trying to deal with their own particular journeys.

Her experiences have given her a passion to help others who have had problems in dealing with mental health issues.

"If I can help someone else believe that despite their mental health issues they are a valid and valued human being, then writing this book will have the result I want."

bshawmh@yahoo.co.uk

After years of feeling an outsider, Becky is now an established author with contributions to academic journals and books.